Issued under the authority of the Home Office (Fire Department)

Manual of Firemanship

A survey of the science of fire-fighting

Book 8
Building construction and structural fire protection

LONDON: HMSO

Applications for reproduction should be made to HMSO
First published 1975
Second edition 1992
Third impression 1995

ISBN 0 11 341038 7

628,92/

Preface

In the last 40 years new buildings in the U.K. have changed considerably. Town centres, shopping malls, factories, offices, residential accommodation etc. have been, and are being, constructed using techniques and materials unheard of in the first half of the century. This has posed problems for the Fire Service, legislators, fire research organisations, insurance companies etc. concerned with the safety of people who work in, or resort to, these premises. An elaborate system of building controls has emerged to ensure that, in the public interest, buildings in the U.K. are constructed to retard the spread of fire both within them and between them. To ensure the safe evacuation of their occupants a very sophisticated set of regulations and techniques has been developed.Government, insurance companies and others have set up testing stations to establish criteria on the behaviour of building materials in fire.

However, firefighters should remember that, notwithstanding legislation controls, tests etc., each building is a conglomeration of materials put together in a particular and, almost always, unique way. Therefore, that building's reaction to a fire, or explosion, can never be accurately forecast. Each material used may have a British Standard assigned to it and may have passed numerous tests but its reaction in fire will be affected by the reaction of the other materials and by the reaction of the contents of the building. The more knowledge firefighters have about a building, especially if they are lucky enough to watch it being constructed, the more likely they are to appreciate its possible reaction to a fire. Every opportunity should be taken to visit buildings, especially those under construction, right up to their internal finishing. This Book is divided into 4 Parts: Building Materials; Elements of Structure; Internal Fire Loading; Building Design. "Internal Fire Loadings" has been included as they appear to have become an important factor in fires in buildings. The materials used in furnishing, cladding and decorating interiors of offices, hotels, places of public resort etc. have contributed to some spectacular, and often fatal, fires in recent times around the world.

Home Office
1992

Metrication

List of SI units for use in the Fire Service

Quantity and basic or derived SI unit and symbol	Approved unit of measurement	Conversion factor
Length metre (m)	kilometre (km) metre (m) millimetre (mm)	1km = 0.621 mile 1m = 1.093 yards = 3.279 feet 1mm = 0.039 inch
Area square metre (m²)	square kilometre (km²) square metre (m²) square millimetre (mm²)	1km² = 0.386 mile² 1m² = 1.196 yards² = 10.764 feet² 1mm² = 0.002 inch²
Volume cubic metre (m³)	cubic metre (m³) litre (l) (= 10⁻³m³)	1m³ = 35.7 feet³ 1 litre = 0.22 gallon
Volume, flow cubic metre per second (m³/s)	cubic metre per second (m³/s) litres per minute (l/min)	1m³/s = 35.7 feet ³/s 1l/min = 0.22 gall/min
Mass kilogram (kg)	kilogram (kg) tonne (t)	1kg = 2.205 lbs 1t = 0.984 ton
Velocity metre per second (m/s)	metre per second (m/s) international knot (kn) (= 1.852km/h) kilometre per hour (km/h)	1m/s = 3.281 feet/second 1km/h = 0.621 mile/hour
Acceleration metre per second² (m/s²)	metre/second² (m/s²)	1m/s² = 3.281 feet/second² = 0.102 'g'
Force newton (N)	kilonewton (kN) newton (n)	1kN = 0.1 ton force 1N = 0.225 lb force

Quantity and basic or derived SI unit and symbol	Approved unit of measurement	Conversion factor
Energy, work joule (J) (= 1Nm)	joule (J) Kilojoule (kJ) Kilowatt/hour (kW/h)	1kJ = 0.953 British Thermal Unit 1J = 0.738 foot lb force
Power watt (W) (= 1J/s = 1Nm/s)	kilowatt (kW) watt (W)	1kW = 1.34 horsepower 1W = 0.735 foot lb force/ second
Pressure newton/metre^2 (N/m^2)	bar (= 10^{5}N/m^2) millibar (mbar) (= 10^{2}N/m^2) metrehead (= 0.0981 bar	1 bar = 0.991 atmosphere 1 bar = 14.5 lb force/in^2 1mbar = 0.0288 inch Hg 1 metrehead = 3.28 foot head
Heat, quantity of heat joule (J)	joule (J) kilojoule (kJ)	1kJ = 0.953 British Thermal Unit
Heat flow rate watt	watt (W) kilowatt (kW)	1W = 3.41 British Thermal Units/hour 1kW = 0.953 British Thermal Unit/Second
Specific energy, calorific value, specific latent heat joule/kilogram (J/kg) joule/m^3 (J/m^3)	kilojoule/kilogram (kJ/kg) kilojoule/m^3 (kJ/m^3) megajoule/m^3 (MJ/m^3)	1kJ/kg = 0.43 British Thermal Unit/lb 1kJ/m^3 = 0.0268 British Thermal Unit/ft^3
Temperature degree Celsius (°C)	degree Celsius (°C)	1 degree Celsius = 1 degree Centigrade

Contents

Part 1
Building materials

Introduction
Chapter 1 The character and use of building materials

General

Chapter 2 Fire testing

Part 2
Elements of structure

Introduction

Chapter 3 General notes on elements of structure – legislation

Chapter 4 True elements of structure

Chapter 5 Other elements of structure

Part 3
Building design

Introduction
Chapter 6 Compartmentation

Chapter 7 Fire spread

Chapter 8 Access to buildings

Chapter 9 Building Construction

Part 4
Interior fire loading

Introduction

Chapter 10 Statistics, hazards and legislation

Chapter 11 Guidance in respect of contents of buildings

Part 5
Examples of buildings

Introduction

Chapter 12 Residential and institutional buildings

Chapter 13 Commercial and industrial buildings

Chapter 14 Public assembly buildings and Town Centres

Chapter 15 Air supported, underground and unfenestrated buildings

Part 6
Services in buildings

Chapter 16 Services in buildings

List of Plates

13 Interior of an ultra-modern hotel.The central lift shaft can be seen left. Note the fire detector left of the sculpture and unopenable windows to the atrium.
Photo: Heathrow Sterling Hotel

14 A nucleus designed hospital built onto an older complex top left.
Photo: Ahrends, Burton and Koralek

15 Leisure centre constructed of glulam showing some of the spans and curves achievable in this type of material.
Photo: Technical Timber Services

16 Modern office construction with atrium. Fire detectors are visible at second floor level.
Photo: The Fitzroy Robinson Partnership

17 Interior of offices under construction (see Plate 18).
Photo: Richard Turpin

18 Exterior of Plate 17 showing almost total glazing with services at each end.
Photo: Richard Turpin

19 Typical atrium of an office block. All the vertical glass is of the "Pyrostop" fire-resistant type.
Photo: Pilkington Glass

20 A high-bay warehouse 155m x 55m x 22m,totally enclosed. The six large smoke outlets are repeated at the other end (see Plate 21).
Photo: Rowntrees Mackintosh

21 The interior of a high-bay warehouse showing automatic picking cranes and the extremely restricted conditions in the racking area.
Photo: Rowntrees Mackintosh

22 Concrete being poured onto a combination of steelwork and polystyrene formers to construct a "honeycomb" roof.
Photo: Essex Fire Brigade

23 Pyrostop fire-resisting glass showing how the intumescent layers react to heat.
Photo: Pilkington Glass

24 Side elevation of a typical modern theatre/concert hall (see Plate 25).
Photo: RHWL Partnership.

25 Interior of the theatre/concert hall illustrated in Plate 24.
Photo: RHWL Partnership

26 Pyrostop fire-resisting glass providing fire separation to a staircase in a public library.
Photo: Pilkington Glass

27 A suspended fabric roof to modern laboratories.
   Photo: Michael Hopkins and Partners

28 Large fixed glazing upstand over a shopping mall. The surface in the foreground is a rubberised flexible membrane providing weatherproofing for the roof.
   Photo: Essex Fire Brigade

29 Polystyrene insulating sheeting placed between the inner wall and the brick cladding.
   Photo: Essex Fire Brigade

30 A specially designed cladding system fitted to an inner hollow-brick wall.
   Photo: Langley London Ltd

31 An example where the strawboard roof lining assisted the spread of the fire.
   Photo: Tyne and Wear Fire Brigade

32 Blockwork wall severely distorted but still intact following a fire.
   Photo: Cheshire Fire Brigade

Part 1
Building materials

An architect will usually design a building using those materials which he, and his client, agree will suit the required endurance, probable use and relevant building controls and, of course, come within the economic parameters set down.

The building controls include certain standards required to ensure that the behaviour of a building, in a fire situation, is satisfactory.

Firefighters must, therefore, try to be as familiar as possible with the properties of materials in so far as they could affect the safety of the public, themselves and the building.

As pointed out in the Preface, the characteristics of individual components of a building will be affected by other components, especially in a fire situation. Firefighters are taught to detect signs of dangerous developments in a building and they should enlarge this knowledge by experience and observation.

This Part deals with many of the types of building materials in use and gives examples of classifying tests used in the United Kingdom.

The point must be made here that fire tests are usually carried out in test rigs which attempt to simulate, as accurately as possible, the kind of situations the material under test could be involved in at a fire. Unfortunately, there are an almost infinite variety of different fire situations which could involve any material and it is impossible to simulate them all. In a real fire situation such factors as:

(1) the severity of the fire

(2) how long the material has been involved

(3) the position of the material eg. wall, floor, ceiling, cladding, suspended.

(4) how the material is fixed to adjoining material

(5) reaction between the adjoining materials

(6) the reaction of the material to the extinguishing medium used

(7) the standard of construction, workmanship etc.

all have a bearing on its behaviour.

Primarily it is the contents of a building that give rise to the danger of fire and any system of tests is designed to try and control the level of the fire risk down to an acceptable standard. The fact that materials used in construction have satisfactorily attained a test requirement will not abolish the risk of fire or prevent it but should have a mitigating affect on fire development.

Chapter 1
The character and use of building materials

General

This first chapter is based on a list of the materials in general use for construction of buildings and their contents. It indicates the uses of these materials and describes their properties insofar as they concern firefighters; these include, where appropriate, their ignitability, fire propagation and/or flame spread characteristics, their behaviour when involved in fire and something of the dangers, if any, that they can present in the course of fire-fighting operations. It is impracticable, however, to provide detail of this kind to cover every possible situation in which a material might be used and every form or combination of forms in which it may appear.

One point of importance in the fire testing of materials deserves mention at this introductory stage and will be referred to again in this text. This is the difference between materials which possess their fire resistant qualities inherently and those whose qualities are added to them at some stage. By 'inherently' it is meant that the quality or qualities reside in the physical and chemical composition of the material itself, so that the material will always possess them while it continues to be that material. On the other hand, various forms of treatment are available for different materials which will improve their fire resistant qualities: sometimes this involves surface application, sometimes impregnation. In the case of some plastic materials, particularly, there are techniques of adding substances at some stage in manufacture; one might think that this would produce 'inherent' qualities in the finished material, but this is not necessarily so. Any process which might result in an uneven distribution of the additive through the material must be regarded with some reserve.

It is common to find that regulating or purchasing authorities tend to distinguish between materials with an inherent fire resistant quality and those of applied quality in favour of the former. This is due to various factors, the most important of which is uncertainty as to whether the quality is permanent after it has been added and, if not, whether it will last the life of the material in the given situation.

1 Timber

Although there exists examples of timber-framed houses dating back to Tudor times it would be fair to say that the vast majority of houses constructed in timber in this country have been built since 1964-65. Because this form of construction enables a wide range of claddings to be used (e.g. brick outer skins, tile hanging or cement rendering on metal laths), in addition to timber – which itself can be fixed to otherwise traditional brick houses – it is not always obvious whether or not a house is timber-framed. The period mentioned began with the introduction, for the first time, of national building regulations. These, together with accumulated knowledge from other countries having a long and continuing history of timber dwellings, have resulted in standards of construction being adopted in Britain which make the modern timber-framed house once completed, with its fire protective linings, as safe as the more traditional forms.

For centuries timber has commonly been used structurally for floors, roofs, beams and columns, internal partitioning and staircases. More recently it has been used in the construction of a wide range of buildings and structures from homes to leisure centres and bridges.

As one would expect, timber is combustible and there are various flame retardant treatments that can assist in making wood more difficult to ignite. There are two types of flame retardant treatments for timber;

a. Surface coatings – painted onto the timber surface with little or no penetration into the wood. Some doubt exists as to the permanency over a period of time.

b. impregnation – using a combination of pressure and vacuum this process 'drives' the liquid into the timber

This is a type of permanent treatment but it may affect the cosmetic appearance of the timber in moist atmospheres.

However, the performance of timber in real fires is frequently far superior to unprotected, non-combustible materials such as steel and aluminium for the following reasons:

(1) Timber does not expand significantly under the influence of heat (in fact, it may shrink slightly) and buildings reliant upon timber for structural purposes are not likely to suffer sudden collapse brought about by 'unrestrained' expansion.

(2) BS 476: Part 5 comes to the conclusion that timber in sizes normally used for construction purposes is defined as '...not easily ignitable.'

(3) Timber has the inherent ability to protect itself; the build-up of charcoal on the surface of burning timber limits the availability of oxygen thereby insulating the remainder of the section.

(4) It has been established that the burning or charring rate is predictable and varies only slightly with species of timber and not on the severity of the fire. 'Sacrificial' timber built into the construction may be consumed by a fire before the structural core is attacked.

Laminated timber has become popular in Britain and has been used for decades in European countries such as Scandinavia, France and

Germany. This type of timber keeps its structural integrity and its cosmetic appearance is one of its attributes. Spectacular spans of over 150 metres can be achieved thereby reducing the requirement for connectors which can represent a weak link in any structure.

2 Stone

The types of stone principally employed in building are granite, sandstone and limestone. Igneous rocks, such as granite, contain free quartz, which has the peculiar property of expanding very rapidly at 575°C and completely shattering the rock. Considerable spalling at the surface may occur in a fire and thin sections of stone may disintegrate entirely. Limestones are composed principally of calcium carbonate, which decomposes at about 800°C into free lime and carbon dioxide. The change is gradual with little alteration in volume, and as heat is absorbed in the process, the interior of a block of limestone may be protected by the outer skin. Water used in fire fighting will slake away the quicklime so formed and will cause the outer skin to fall away.

Sandstone generally comes between granite and limestone in fire behaviour and may shrink and crack in a fire. Stone is, in general, a good heat insulator, but is inferior to brick when subjected to continuous heat, because of its tendency to spall or split into pieces, especially when water is suddenly applied. Stonework should always be carefully watched for signs of cracking when it is necessary to work beneath or near it.

Stone and granite is now normally used for facings and decoration and its failure in the event of a fire is unlikely to affect the stability of the structure.

3 Bricks

Bricks have traditionally been made from clay and similar materials which have been moulded or pressed into shape and fired in a kiln; these are generally referred to as clay-fired bricks. For many years now, concrete bricks and calcium silicate bricks have also been produced. Concrete bricks are made from cement and a fine aggregate, such as sand or a fine crushed stone. Calcium silicate bricks, which are also known as sand-lime or flint-lime bricks, are made by treating a mixture of lime and a siliceous aggregate in high-pressure steam, the process being known as autoclaving.

Although there are many varieties of each of the three types of brick, and different types of mortar may be used for bedding them, no distinction is made between them in classifying the behaviour of brick walls subjected to a fire on one side. The important features of a brick wall affecting its fire resistance are thickness, the beneficial effects of applied rendering or plastering, especially lightweight plaster or special insulating plaster, and whether or not it is load-bearing. Large perforations or cavities in some bricks may make them susceptible to spalling of small areas of the exposed surfaces.

4 Cement (including Glass Reinforced Cement (GRC))

Cement is a fine powder – usually made with various types of Portland cement – which forms part of a combination of materials to make concrete. It reacts chemically with water and the longer the drying process the more strength is developed.

Glass reinforced cement, with its rapidly increasing applications in construction, is a composite material consisting of cement and a small proportion of glass fibres. The addition of GRC reinforcement enhances the strength and toughness of the cement; however, there is some doubt as to the long term durability of GRC.

Two particular characteristics of cement can be changed by the addition of small proportions of other materials. For example, cement is inherently fire resistant but the addition of pulverised fuel ash (PFA) can increase that fire resistance. Cement is also known to shrink considerably when drying and a small amount of sand added to the GRC ensures that this does not happen.

5 Concrete

Concrete consists of aggregates such as sand, gravel or crushed stone combined with cement and water. When first mixed together it forms a material capable of setting and hardening to produce a solid, rock-like mass.

Concrete can be produced having a wide range of properties such as high compressive strength, durability, thermal insulation and fire protection. All these qualities largely depend on the materials and the proportions used in the mix. When concrete is heated, it expands due to thermal expansion of the materials, but the hardened cement paste also shrinks as a result of loss of moisture by drying out. As a result the overall change is not easily predicted and internal stresses can be set up within the concrete. In a severe fire, spalling of the surface material occurs and is aggravated if the hot concrete is suddenly chilled, for example with a jet of water. Concrete made with limestones or lightweight aggregates, are very much less susceptible to spalling than those made with more dense aggregates, hence the fire resistance of structural concrete is classified differently according to the type of aggregate used.

a. Reinforced concrete

Except for concrete bricks and blocks, concrete is rarely used for structural purposes without being reinforced because it is relatively weak in tension and prone to crack. In the early days of reinforced concrete construction, reinforcement consisted of plain round mild steel-bars, but high tensile steel reinforcement – hot rolled bars or cold-worked bars of different types – have been introduced over the years. In reinforced concrete, the steel is not stressed until loads are imposed on the structural member.

b. Pre-stressed concrete

Pre-stressed concrete is a form of structural concrete in which tensile steel tendons are stressed against the length of concrete, which is thus put into compression, before imposed loads are applied. Pre-stressed concrete is sub-divided into pre-tensioned and post-tensioned systems (see Figs. 4.7 and 4.8)

(1) Pre-tensioned concrete

This has the tendons stretched and anchored independently of the concrete before the concrete is cast around them and allowed to harden. The tendons are then released from their anchorage but, because they are now bonded to the hardened concrete, they are anchored by the concrete and put it into compression.

(2) Post-tensioned concrete

This is cast with ducts through which the tendons are threaded and then stressed after it has hardened, each tendon being anchored against the concrete. The tendons may remain unbonded, but often the space between the tendons and the ducts is grouted so that the tendons become effectively bonded to the concrete and at the same time are protected against corrosion.

No distinction is drawn between the different forms of pre-stressed concrete in assessing their fire resistance.

c. Fire resistance of concrete

As was mentioned earlier, the fire resistance of concrete itself is determined by the aggregate used in its make-up. However, the fire resistance of structural concrete, whether reinforced or pre-stressed, is determined primarily by the protection of the steel against an excessive rise in the temperature. This is afforded by the concrete cover, ie. the concrete between the surface of the member and the nearest surface of the embedded steel. Generally, the greater the amount of cover, the longer the period of fire resistance. The so-called 'critical' temperature for steel is about 550°C for mild steel and about 400°C for high tensile steel, but in neither case is there a sudden change in the properties of the steel. These are the temperatures at which they lose about half their cold strength and therefore at which most of the design factor of safety is likely to be used up. In a fire, structural concrete does not normally collapse suddenly – it may deflect considerably under load, and floors may suffer local break down, but even after a severe fire most concrete structures are safe enough to be reinstated to perform their original functions.

6 Metals

Whilst a number of different metals are used to some extent in building, only iron and steel are normally used for those parts which have to carry any load. Cast iron possesses relatively little strength in tension, but is capable of sustaining a considerable load in compression. Cast iron was very widely used in the 19th century for beams and columns, and even now, there are many buildings in use which are supported by cast iron columns and beams. Iron and steel used in the construction of a building are not combustible and present no risk of fire spread from direct burning.

Unprotected metal surfaces may, none the less, constitute a serious risk in a fire because all metals heat up and expand when exposed to fire and are also a potential cause of fire spread by conduction. Unprotected metal which is used to carry a load also presents the even more serious danger of rapid collapse when excessively heated. Structural steel, for example, loses two-thirds of its strength at 593°C and, in proportion to the amount and direction of the load to which it is subjected, begins to sag and twist. This is by no means an abnormal temperature in even a moderate fire – the danger of the failure of unprotected load-bearing metal work cannot be over-emphasised.

A 10 metres steel joist, for example, will expand 60mm for a 500°C rise of temperature, and where it is built into a loadbearing wall, such expansion may cause collapse. In a framed building, the failure of a single beam or column is unlikely to cause more than a local collapse. It is clear then that all structural steel must be protected either by solid or hollow protection. (See Part 2, Section 1).

Because it is prone to rapid corrosion, stainless steel is invariably coated, normally with a protective metal coating in the first place, and, outside this, frequently with some form of mineral and resin mixture. This is liable to produce the anomaly that, whereas steel itself is non-combustible, a protected steel sheet of the type described may well have a surface spread of flame of Class 1, 2 or even 3.

Increasing use is being made of aluminium and its alloys for structural and cladding members and this has created new fire problems. The advantages of using aluminium alloy in buildings are:

(i)   a reduction in the weight of the structure;

(ii)   resistance to corrosion;

(iii)   ease of handling and working; and

(iv)   the high strength to weight ratio.

The disadvantages are:

(v)   the vary rapid loss of strength in fire (stability is affected at 100°C to 225°C);

(vi)   the high expansion rate (approximately twice that of steel);

(vii)   its very low melting point (pure aluminium melts at 660°C).

Lead was principally employed for internal plumbing, flashings and roof coverings. It melts at 327°C and precautions should therefore be taken against injury from molten metal when working beneath a lead roof at a fire in older buildings. Copper and zinc are also used for roof coverings but their melting points are much higher and the metal usually oxidises away under the influence of the fire so that there is rarely much danger from falling molten material. Bronze has a melting point about 1000°C, but is normally only used for decorative grilles, handrails, etc and occasionally for window frames.

7 Glass

Glass is non-combustible and will not, therefore, contribute fuel to a fire or directly assist a fire to spread. At one time, glass would have constituted a major weakness in a wall, door or screen because it would break and fall out. Fire resisting glazing not only provides an effective barrier to the spread of smoke and flames, it can also provide protection against radiant heat in a fire.

Architects and designers are no longer restricted by solid materials such as timber and metals. Today in its various fire safety forms, glass offers new dimensions and designers can create the feeling of more light and space with glass. In high security areas such as Banks and Building Societies, the glass may be specially toughened to resist vandal attacks.

It is imperative however with fire resistant glass that the whole glazing system, including the frame and method of fixing must have fire resistance, not just the glass itself. BS 476, Part 22 gives guidance in this area.

a. Wired glass

Wired glass is generally 6mm thick and is manufactured by sandwiching an electronically welded steel mesh between two layers of molten glass in one continuous rolling process. Wired glass will crack very early in a fire but the steel mesh sandwiched in the centre of the glass holds it together if it has been broken by impact or by thermal shock. Because the integrity and stability are retained in a fire, the spread of smoke and flame is prevented even though the glass may be badly damaged.

b. Multi-laminate glass

This relatively new fire-resisting glass is manufactured from multi-laminate panes of float glass with clear intumescent interlayers. On exposure to fire the intumescent layers expand to form an opaque shield which forms an effective barrier to smoke and flames and prevents the transfer of radiant and conductive heat (see Plates 23 and 26).

c. Heat treated fire glass

This type of glass is wire free and as such can be fractured early on in a fire if subjected to thermal shock. The important aspect here is the 'edge' of the glass. This must be protected from the full force of the fire. It is absolutely vital, (as with all windows), however that the glass is installed properly to ensure that it performs correctly and does not fracture.

8 Building Boards

Whatever the cause of a fire within a building, the surfaces of wall and ceilings will contribute to the fire if they are ignited. Ensuring that these surfaces are non-combustible or at least, very difficult to ignite, means that, if a fire does start, its rate of growth will be reduced. It is also desirable to keep to a minimum the amount of smoke or toxic fumes given off from this type of surface if involved in a fire, particularly those lining escape routes.

A wide range of materials are used in the manufacture of sheets of varying sizes, thickness and fire resistance. They bear many different trade names but may be classified generally in one of the following groups:

    (a) fibre building boards
    (b) plaster boards
    (c) asbestos boards
    (d) plywood boards
    (e) block boards
    (f) plastic boards.

a. Fibre building boards

Fibre building boards are manufactured in a wide range of sheet materials, usually more than 1.5 mm thick. They are made from actual wood fibres or woody plants and derive their basic strength and cohesion by the felting together of the fibres themselves, and from their inherent adhesive properties. Bonding, impregnating or other agents, including fire retardants, may be added during or after manufacture to modify particular properties.

Fibre building boards fall into two major groups according to whether the board has been compressed in a hydraulic press during manufacture or not. The non-compressed type is termed insulating board (softboard). This is used in sheet form and as tiles. Bitumen impregnated insulating board also comes within this category; it is used for sheathing timber-framed buildings and for roof-sarking (lining), the bitumen content gives it a high resistance to moisture. In the second group are medium boards of low or high density from 6-13 mm thick and hardboards. Standard hardboard is a dense sheet material 2-13 mm thick with one smooth face and a mesh pattern on the reverse. Tempered hardboard, 3-13 mm thick has high strength and water resistance. It is made by impregnating standard hardboard with oils and resins, usually immediately after pressing, and then applying further heat treatment. Building boards of this group are not easily ignitable but all are combustible.

b. Plaster boards

Plaster boards for interior use are composed of a core of set gypsum or anhydrite plaster enclosed between, and firmly bonded to, two sheets of heavy paper to increase their tensile strength. In a fire the exposed paper face may burn away making it relatively easy to break up the non-combustible gypsum core, but until this happens, the plaster board will retard the spread of fire.

Vermiculite is a clay-mineral which expands to many times its original volume when subjected to high temperature. It is incorporated in plasterboards to give it a superior fire resistant rating than ordinary linings. Plasterboard and vermiculite can also be mixed with other products such as silicate which again is non-combustible and does not emit smoke when involved in fire.

c. Asbestos boards

It goes without saying that asbestos does not form a part of the composition of today's products but cement sheets or insulating or wallboards may still be found in older buildings. When subjected to fire, the amount of smoke given off is negligible.

d. Plywood boards

Plywood boards are made up of thin wood laminations laid in alternate directions to increase their strength. Their susceptibility to fire depends on the type of timber used and the overall thickness of the board. The type of bonding material may have some bearing on the development of a fire.

e. Block boards

These are made from a core of separate wood blocks bonded together and finished externally with a veneer or plastic overlay to give the appearance of a homogenous board. They are produced in many grades and qualities and their behaviour in fire varies accordingly.

f. Plastic boards

Plastic boards are composed of organic materials, e.g. paper, linen, sawdust or woodchips, bonded together with synthetic resins and subjected to heat and pressure. Phenolic laminates are rigid boards made of sheets of special paper impregnated with phenol-formaldehyde and urea-formaldehyde. This type of board has good fire resisting properties and usually incorporates a flame retardant substance in its manufacture. Resin-bonded sawdust (or woodchip) boards are sawdust and/or woodchips bonded with synthetic resins, and are man-made timbers; their behaviour in fire is dependent on their surface treatment.

There are many other types of popular plastics available. One which has increased in use is expanded polystyrene which is often used as wall and ceiling tiles because of its good thermal insulation qualities. Although this is available in flame retardant grades it is known to burn fairly rapidly and often softens and collapses. Foamed polyurethane in flexible and rigid forms are also excellent thermal insulators and are used in various applications as a weather resistant coating. Again this is available in flame retardant grades but generally burns rapidly producing thick dark smoke.

9 Building slabs

Building slabs can come in a variety of sizes and are generally made out of long wood fibres mixed with portland cement and compressed. They are combustible but the wood is chemically treated to provide fire resistance and often are water resistant as well. Slabs are used for roof decking and provide sound and heat insulation.

10 Building blocks

Building blocks, like bricks, are used for the construction of walls of all types, and they have become popular because of the savings resulting from the improved productivity when laying units larger than bricks. Blocks are generally made of concrete combined with various types of aggregates which give the block different loadbearing qualities whilst others are designed purely for insulating qualities.

Hollow-fired clay blocks combine a clay aggregate to produce a particularly light weight block. The hollow interior is filled with polyurethane foam to give it excellent thermal properties.

Their fire-resisting qualities are generally better the greater the thickness and the smaller the proportion of voids. In a fire, the face of the block exposed to the fire, whether used in a partition or a floor, may spall as a result of the unequal expansion of the material in the block as the temperature rises.

There are several types of concrete block which are made in a variety of thickness from 50mm to over 100 mm thick. Their size and whether they are solid or hollow decide if they are to be used as loadbearing walls or non-loadbearing partitions. Most are moulded by special machines from concrete made with normal dense or lightweight aggregates.

Aerated concrete is made by a completely different process using cement and sand and/or pulverised-fuel ash (PFA) or cement and lime. The addition of fine aluminium powder causes the formation of numerous small air cells. A large 'cake' is produced which is cut into pieces and autoclaved (high pressure steam curing).

For the purpose of determining fire resistance, machine-made blocks are divided into two classes according to the type of aggregate used in their manufacture. Class 1 blocks – those with a higher fire resistance for a given thickness – are made from lightweight aggregates; Class 2 blocks which, for the same period of fire resistance, require a slightly greater thickness, are made from naturally dense aggregates other than limestone. Slightly different values apply to aerated concrete blocks; compared with Class 1 aggregate blocks, loadbearing walls with 240 or 360 minutes of fire resistance should be a little thicker, but non-loadbearing walls with low periods of resistance can be thinner. All types provide a high degree of fire resistance with little risk of collapse or deterioration and, therefore, give effective compartmentation (see Plate 32).

The fire resistance of block walls is improved if they are plastered on both sides and especially so if a lightweight plaster, such as vermiculite-gypsum plaster, is used.

11 Insulating material

a. Cavities

In order to reduce heat transmission in hollow spaces such as those between double partitions between an exterior wall and an internal lining, in a floor or in a roof, they are frequently filled with materials which are of a loose fibrous nature and have a low conductivity. Many substances have been used for this purpose, including such combustible materials as cork, sawdust and peat. Modern research, however, has produced noncombustible substitutes such as rock or glass wool, foamed slag, vermiculite, etc. (see Plates 29 and 30) and those are now replacing the older materials in new buildings, although by no means all insulating materials now being employed are non-combustible. Polystyrene is well known for its good thermal properties and comes in various forms such as rigid or flexible sheets, in granulated form or as a spray – it has the disadvantage however of having little fire resistance. To enable them to be laid rapidly in a position, insulating materials are sometimes sandwiched between layers of bituminous paper or felt and are then known as 'quiltings'. Combustible quiltings, eg. those with a wood or seaweed base, enable a fire to travel easily through concealed wall and ceiling spaces, the plaster or board lining preventing effective extinction until it is removed. This type of insulation is to be found in older buildings and is not a process employed in the construction of todays modern buildings.

b. Spray-on insulation and intumescent seals

It is essential that the structure of a building is safe under fire conditions and retains its integrity long enough for the brigade to carry out its duties.

Since the advent of sprayed asbestos, new technology has developed a wide range of spray-on products like vermiculite-cement and sprayed mineral fibre, some of which are designed to withstand high intensity fires which might be experienced, for example, in the petro-chemical industry.

Intumescent strip seals and acrylic mastic have been developed to provide protection and maintain fire resistance in gaps and joints which are flexible enough for structural movement. These various types of internal and external insulation material not only help a building to reduce heat transmission or protect it in the event of fire; it also helps to reduce condensation and deaden sound.

12 Paint

Paint is used both as a preservative and as a decoration principally for woodwork, steelwork and plaster, and is sometimes applied to brickwork. Paint consists of a pigment (normally a powdered solid) carried in a vehicle (a liquid) which, by chemical action and evaporation, allows the film to harden. Almost all paints (with the exception of fire-retardant paints mentioned later) are flammable, but the film ordinarily is so thin that it has no appreciable effect on a fire, although under certain conditions, it can foster surface spread. Sometimes, however, when many coats of paint have been applied over a number of years, the film may be sufficiently thick to become flammable and constitute a fire risk. The paint on steelwork, for instance, can ignite if heated sufficiently by a fire, eg. the far side of a bulkhead in a ship fire. Where appearance is unimportant, tar or bituminous paint is sometimes used and the film may then be sufficiently thick to burn even though applied to steelwork with no other combustible material present.

Fire-retardant paints are occasionally used to protect timber and are of two types. One type is a fairly heavy-based paint which will not inhibit combustion completely, but will do much to reduce flaming, whilst the other, which is termed 'intumescent paint', will, when subjected to heat, bubble up and form a layer of air cells which acts as an insulation between the heat of the fire and the timber underneath. This type of paint is very effective and can be obtained in colour or as a transparent covering.

The development of intumescent coatings proved to be a technological breakthrough. Originally, this type of paint was designed to retard flame spread but has now been developed to react chemically to heat exposure by undergoing a physical change. On reaching temperatures in excess of 200°C (Paint Research Association figures), the paint develops into a thick insulating foam which can protect steel for long periods of time depending on the thickness of the coatings.

13 Plastics

Reference has already been made in section 10(f) to 'plastic boards' but, in recent years, there has been a considerable increase in the use of plastics in building construction. The term 'plastics' is a generic name for a group of materials based on synthetic or modified natural polymers (see the Manual, Book 1, Chapter 9) which at some stage of manufacture can be formed to shape by flow, aided in many cases by heat and pressure. They can be *thermosetting,* ie. they will not soften significantly on heating to a temperature below decomposition temperature, or *thermoplastic,* ie. capable of being softened by the application of heat.

Plastic materials of different degrees of stiffness are described as rigid, semi-rigid and non-rigid plastics. Reinforced plastics consist essentially of polymer combined with fibrous material to enhance its mechanical strength. This term is most commonly used for thermosetting polyester resin with glass fibres (GRP). One of the uses of this material is as external cladding in the form of moulded panels in building systems. It can be formed to a wide variety of shapes, colours and textures; components made from it are light in weight and its mouldability allows the incorporation of detail that would be impossible to achieve with other materials.

Cellular plastics are made up of a mass of cells in which the matrix is a plastics material.

Foamed plastics are cellular plastics made mainly from liquid starting materials, eg. polyurethane foam.

Expanded plastics are made by stamping or cutting plastics sheet and stretching to form open meshes, in the same way as expanded metal is formed.

The problems of tensile strength and compressive strengths of these materials for their possible use as structural elements have not yet been fully resolved and, except for small complete structures, they are not used for loadbearing members. A substantial amount of plastics material will, however, be encountered within buildings in the form of thermal insulation, service pipes, wall, floor and ceiling covering, furniture, furnishings and fitments. Translucent pvc sheeting is widely used for roof lighting and clear acrylic resins used for shaped lighting panels as in domes. Plastics materials cover such a wide range of substances that their properties and behaviour in fire can be described only in very broad terms. It depends upon the composition and method of manufacture, the free access to air and any support to combustion that may be available. The products of combustion of many plastic materials may be very toxic; again this is dependent on the type of plastic and the combustion of other materials that may be involved in the fire. The face of construction is changing however with the first "system-built" house in Pittsfield, USA, constructed in the main, of plastic around a timber-framed structure. "Systembuilt" construction is already well accepted in Japan and Scandinavia and, with the rising price of labour, may soon find its way to Europe.

Chapter 2
Fire testing

1 General

As pointed out in Chapter 3, all building works, with a few exceptions, within the UK are controlled by legislation. It covers all aspects of construction including structural fire precautions and some means of escape. The principle is to provide for the health, safety and welfare of people and is not, primarily, for safeguarding property or limiting economic loss. The requirements of regulations can be put under the following headings:

(i)   means of escape
(ii)   internal fire spread (surfaces)
(iii)   internal fire spread (structures)
(iv)   external fire spread
(v)   access and facilities for the Fire Service

2 Fire tests

Fire testing, if correctly designed and carried out,may, in some cases, be the only available and reliable indication of a material's behaviour in a given fire situation. It can thus be a vital factor in giving detailed answers to questions put in identifying and assessing fire hazards.

It must be remembered that fire behaves in a complex manner and any information gleaned from a particular fire test must not be over-estimated or taken as a prediction of a probable course of an actual fire. It can only predict the behaviour of the test material in the restricted situation of the test itself. A fire test result that shows an acceptable performance by the tested material can never be taken to guarantee a safe situation.

3 British Standard 476

a. General

BS476 contains the principal criteria for assessing the fire properties of building materials and elements of structure. A great deal of research is currently being undertaken into fire development and the BS476 series are consequently always being kept under review and may be revised or new tests devised.

It must be borne in mind that none of these tests, of themselves, decide the acceptability of the material, they only measure its qualities. It is for the regulations to decide whether these qualities are acceptable in the use that is made of the material. An example would be a material with a certain rate of surface spread of flame which may be acceptable for the roof of a single storey building but entirely unsatisfactory in a corridor which forms part of a means of escape.

b. Parts of the Standard

BS 476 is divided into a number of Parts some of which have been published, some are in the consulting stage and preparation stage and others, although planned, are not very advanced. As a result of an increasing interest in fire testing in relation to reducing fire hazards and controlling the products and elements of structure used in buildings, BS476 Part 10 was produced. This is the "Guide to the principles and application of fire testing". It also stems from a desire to move away from the old method of testing, which was based largely on experience and limited technical data, towards a more rational approach.

The methods specifically designed to assess the response to fire of building products have been allocated Part Numbers 11-19, those for elements of building construction Numbers 20-29 and miscellaneous methods from Number 30 onwards. In order to provide continuity from the old to the new methods the present published series (from 3-8) will be retained as long as necessary but will eventually be phased out. In fact, at the time of writing (1991) Part 8 has been replaced by Parts 20-23 inclusive. Part 8 still remains available since it is referred to in the regulations and legislative documents.

The list of Parts is as follows:

Old Parts

BS476   Part 3   1975   External fire exposure roof test

Part 4   1970   Non-combustibility test for materials

Part 5   1979   Method of test for ignitability

Part 6   1981   Method of test for fire propagation for products

Part 7   1971   Surface spread of flame test for materials

New Parts

Fire tests for Products

Part 11 1982   Method for assessing the heat emission from building material

Part 12   Method of measuring the ignitability of products using direct flame impingement. (under consideration)

Part 13 1987   Method of measuring the ignitability of products subjected to thermal irradiance.

Part 14   Method of measuring the rate of flame spread on surfaces of products.

Part 15 — Method of measuring the rate of heat release of products

Part 16 — Method of measuring the smoke release (obscuration) of products.

Parts 17, 18 — Other methods of testing relating to products.

Fire tests for elements of building construction

Part 20 1987 — Method for the determination of the fire resistance of elements of building construction.

Part 21 1987 — Methods for the determination of the fire resistance of load-bearing elements of building construction.

Part 22 1987 — Methods for the determination of the fire resistance of non-loading bearing elements of building construction.

Part 23 1987 — Methods for the determination of the contribution provided by components and elements to the fire resistance of a structure

Part 24 1987 — Methods for the determination of the fire resistance of elements of construction penetrated by building services.

Parts 25-29 — Other methods related to the determination of fire resistance.

Miscellaneous fire tests

Part 30 — Methods for measuring the performance of flat and sloping roofs exposed to an external fire.

Part 31 1983 — Method for measuring smoke penetration through door sets and shutter assemblies.

Part 32 1989 — Building materials and structures guide to full-scale fire tests within buildings.

c. Some detail of the Parts.

A study of the list in section b. above indicates that Parts 3 - 7 are already in line to be replaced. The present main properties which are thought to influence the behaviour of building materials when involved in fire are:

(i) combustibility

(ii) ignitability

(iii) fire propagation

(iv) rate of surface spread of flame

The list, however, shows that these divisions are going to be sub-divided into areas for more detailed study. For instance, (iv) above, in the present Part 7, has four classes. The highest classification ie. the highest resistance to spread of flame, being Class 1. However, Building Regulations refer to materials of Class 0 which, although not a BS specification, is considered to impose a higher standard than Class 1. This extra category may be included in the new Part 14 together with a new method of testing.

The division of Part 5 into new Parts 12 and 13 is an example of up-grading. Part 13 uses a far more complicated piece of test apparatus and requires 5 specimens for test instead of the 3 in Part 5. It is likely that Part 12 will follow a similar pattern.

d. Detail of Parts 20-23 inclusive.

(i) Part 20

Is an introduction to Parts 21-23 and explains the general principles of the testing. It is used as a base and Parts 21-23 refer back to its sections especially when commenting upon performance criteria.

(ii) Part 21

Here the criteria of failure for the fire resistance of beams and columns refer back to Section 10.2.3. of Part 20.

When determining the fire resistance of floors, flat roofs and walls it refers back to Part 20 Sections 10.2., 10.3. and 10.4. These give criteria on loadbearing capacity, integrity and insulation respectively.

(iii) Part 22

This deals with the fire resistance of partitions, door sets, shutter assemblies, ceiling membranes and glazing. A ceiling membrane is defined as:

"A non-loadbearing element of a building construction designed to provide horizontal fire separation,as distinct from protection, to any floor or roof above"

The criteria of failure here are modifications of Sections 10.3 and 10.4. of Part 20.

(iv) Part 23

This Part determines the contribution of suspended ceilings to the fire resistance of steel beams and the contribution of intumescent seals to the fire resistance of timber door assemblies.Here again reference is made to Sections 10.2.3. and 10.3.2 in Part 20.

4 Example of other standards

a. BS 6336, 1982

This standard gives guidance to those concerned with maintaining acceptable standards of safety from fire and those concerned with fire hazards and fire tests. It sounds a cautionary note on the use of terminology and offers some advice on how to go about the assessment and control of fire hazards when preparing specifications or Codes of Practice. A summary of these is:

(i)   in consultation with experts assess the fire hazards that might arise in the use of the material,product, structure or system.

(ii)   consider what level of fire hazard is acceptable in the use of those materials etc. and how this hazard can be reduced.

(iii)   identify the properties or functions of the material etc. which appear critical in the control of a fire hazard.

(iv)   develop fire tests which will provide information to assist in the assessment and control of the hazard in terms of those properties or functions.

(v)   use,at all times, only terminology that is recommended in this Standard ensuring it is accurate,specific and based on relevant test procedure.

(vi) recognise that the results of a fire test do not guarantee fire safety.

b. PD 6520 1988

This Published Document is to assist those people who want to know the scope and principles of fire test methods of building materials and elements of construction. A short commentary on each test is made.It covers all parts of BS476 and BS2782 "Methods of testing plastics"

5. International and European standards

All British standards either already have European or International equivalent standards or will in the future and those concerned with fire-testing are, obviously, included. The Fire Service can expect to find an increasing number of dual standards quoting ISO (International Standards Organisation) and CEN (Committee on European Norms) numbers together with their British equivalents.

Part 2
Elements of structure

Part 1 dealt with building materials and testing of those materials. This Part discusses elements of structure eg. beams, columns, floors, walls and roofs.

Again, as pointed out in Part 1, all these, in combination, contribute towards the stability of the building.

At the FRS, testing is carried out both on single elements and, where possible, on combinations as would be found in construction.

In a general sense, "elements" will include other features of construction eg. staircases, doors, windows but these do not, usually, contribute to the stability of the building.

The Building Regulations are also looked at in this Part. The emphasis of these has undergone radical change in 1985 and 1991. A fairly general explanation of their intent is included.

The latest changes do not, in fact, come into operation until 1st June 1992 and firefighters should bear this in mind as well as realising that the Regulations are under constant scrutiny and further amendment in the future is a certainty.

Chapter 3
General notes on elements of structure

1 Building Regulations: structural fire precautions

General

When dealing with the construction of buildings, it is necessary to make frequent reference to the Building Regulations. Although these Regulations mainly concern architects and builders, firefighters must have a working knowledge of those parts of the fire section of the Regulations. Later in their careers, a more thorough knowledge of those parts of the Regulations which deal with all forms of structural protection will be necessary, when they will be required to give expert advice on a wide range of subjects dealing with fire prevention and fire protection to other professions allied to the construction industry, to owners and occupies of premises and to the general public.

The *Building Regulations* of England and Wales are made under the *Building Act 1984*. Under this Act provision is made for *Building Regulations* to be dealt with by local authorities or, for the first time, by private 'Approved Inspectors' (AIs). In law, the fire regulations are intended to safeguard the public in and around buildings and not the property or its contents. It naturally follows, however, that ensuring the safety of persons within and about the building must make a valuable contribution towards the protection of the property against the destructive effects of fire.

2 Building Regulations 1991

(1) Building Regulations (BR) 1991 are, themselves a development of the BR 1985, and impose a less detailed form of control than the previous regulations (1976) in that they do not specify constructional details. Instead they lay down "functional requirements"(FR).

There are five FR which appertain to fire protection ie.

B1 Means of escape
B2 Internal fire spread (linings)
B3 Internal fire spread (structure)
B4 External fire spread
B5 Access and facilities for the Fire Service.

As can be seen from the following definitions of the five FR, it is necessary to design and construct a building so that the FR is satisfied.

To assist Architects and builders to conform to the FR a series of "Approved Documents" (AD) accompany the Building Regulations.

They suggest the parameters necessary to satisfy the FR but if the architect, designer, builder etc. has other ideas and can show that these ideas would satisfy the requirements of the BR then they should be approved.

3. Functional requirements

B1. "The building shall be designed and constructed so that there are means of escape, in case of fire, from the building, to a place of safety outside the building, capable of being safely and effectively used at all material times. "

B2. "To inhibit the spread of fire within the building the internal linings shall:

(i) resist the spread of flame over their surfaces and

(ii) have, if ignited, a rate of heat release which is reasonable in the circumstances.

In this paragraph "internal linings" mean the materials lining any partition, wall, ceiling or other internal structure.

B3. (i) "The building shall be designed and constructed so that, in the event of fire, its stability will be maintained for a reasonable period"

(ii) "A wall common to two, or more, buildings, shall be designed and constructed so that it resists the spread of fire between those buildings"

(iii) "To inhibit the spread of fire within a building it shall be sub-divided with fire-resisting construction to an extent appropriate to the size and intended use of the building".

(iv) "The building shall be designed and constructed so that the unseen spread of fire and smoke, within concealed spaces in its structure and fabric, is inhibited".

B4. (i) "The external walls of the building shall resist the spread of fire over the walls and from one building to another having regard to the height, use and position of the building".

(ii) "The roof of the building shall resist the spread of fire over the roof and from one building to another having regard to the use and position of the building".

B5. (i) "The building shall be designed and constructed so as to provide facilities to assist firefighters in the protection of life".

(ii)   Provision shall be made within the site of the building to enable fire appliances to gain access to the building".

In essence there are 3 ways in which the fire safety FR can be met:

(a)   To follow the Approved Document as explained above.

(b)   To comply with the relevant parts of nationally recognised fire precautions standards eg. the BS series 5588. In fact a number of the most common standards for certain specialised uses of premises are referenced in the AD as the guidance that should be used.

(c)   Any way in which the applicant can satisfy the local authority (in consultation with the fire authority) that he/she has complied. This third approach opens the way for engineering solutions and integrated fire safety in particularly innovative buildings where conventional passive fire defence would inhibit design.

4 Active fire defence.

The 1991 BR lay greater emphasis on active fire defence than the ADs in the 1985 BR.

Among the technical recommendations are new provisions for smoke detectors in houses and flats and the provision of sprinklers in certain tall buildings. In fact there are a number of specific references to sprinkler systems and they mainly take the form of concessions, in relation to fire resistance and compartment sizes, where the building is provided with a sprinkler system meeting the relevant recommendations of BS5306: Part 2.

5 Approved Inspectors (AIs)

Mention was made, in para. 1 above, of private "Approved Inspectors" (AIs). Under the Building (Approved Inspectors etc.) Regulations 1985, the Secretary of State can appoint suitably qualified "approved inspectors" who a developer/architect can employ to supervise all the aspects of the Building Regulations which would apply to a particular development or building.

The AI is, in fact, a private building control officer (BCO) and is the equivalent of the local authority BCO. The AI, like the BCO must consult with the fire authority in the usual way.

6 Definition of elements of structure.

a. Approved Document "B" of the Building Regulations defines elements of structure as being:

(i)   any member forming part of the structural frame of a building (Fig. 3. 1(1)) or any beam or column (2) not being a member forming part of a roof structure only;

(ii)   a floor (3) including a compartment floor but not the lowest floor of the building or a platform floor;

(iii)   an external wall (4)

(iv)   separating wall (5)

(v)   a compartment wall (6)

(vi)   a structure enclosing a protected shaft (7)

(vii) a load-bearing wall or load-bearing part of a wall (8)

(viii) a gallery (9)

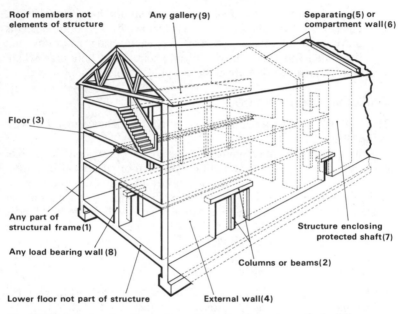

Roof members not elements of structure

Any gallery (9)

Separating(5) or compartment wall(6)

Floor (3)

Any part of structural frame(1)

Any load bearing wall (8)

Structure enclosing protected shaft(7)

Columns or beams(2)

Lower floor not part of structure

External wall(4)

Fig. 3.1 Sketch showing the various elements of structure of a building.

The other elements such as stairs, roofs, partitions doors etc. which are also necessary to complete a building are discussed in Chapter 5.

The function of each of the elements of structure, in the majority of buildings, is to carry the loads placed upon them.

These loads are, principally, :

(a) The "Dead Load" which is the weight of all parts of the building itself which is imposed on the elements. These are constant.

(b) The "Imposed Load" which consists of the people, furniture, machinery and materials expected to be in the building when it is occupied.

(c) The "Wind Load" which means all loads due to the effects of wind pressure or suction.

7 The Factor of Safety

Complex design calculations are necessary to resolve these loadings and a factor of safety is applied to ensure that only materials and elements of structure of sufficient strength and adequate stability are used in construction.

The existence of a factor of safety in all well built structures is useful to a firefighter. An experienced firefighter may be able to judge, within limits, the extent to which the factor of safety has been reduced by burning, heat or distortion of various parts of the building.

By an assessment of the remaining factor of safety the firefighter may be able to decide whether it is safe to work, in a fire, underneath parts of the structure which have been partially destroyed. For example, it may happen that a wooden beam has been considerably burned or charred and yet retains a sufficient factor of safety to allow firefighting to proceed beneath it without danger. By the destruction of some support, a beam could become a cantilever and still retain enough strength to be safe. Walls and columns have to carry not only the vertical loads but, also, to withstand the overturning effects imposed by wind loads and by eccentric loading.

Many of the stresses in a building are altered in a fire for heat affects different building materials in different ways. Readily flammable materials such as wood may simply burn, although this will depend largely on their cross-sectional area. Metals will, expand, distort or melt. Concrete and stone may contract, expand or violently disintegrate. Sudden cooling after heating can cause cast-iron or stone to crack and floor loads are often vastly increased by debris and the weight of water poured into the building.

In a fire all these changes will be taking place simultaneously and, as will be emphasised elsewhere in this Book, an ability to interpret the inter-reactions comes with experience and firefighters should take every opportunity to learn. A minor collapse in one part can trigger a larger collapse, a dust explosion, a release of chemicals, gas, etc. The posting of Safety Officers with means of rapid communication and warning, are essential at any large incident.

A building reduced to its simplest essentials may usually be said to consist of: foundations to transmit the load of the structure to the ground without appreciable movement or shifting, walls, floors and roof. It has been said that a structure does not become a building until it possesses a roof.

8 Fire tests of elements of construction (general)

Parts 20 - 23 of BS 476:1972 (see Chapter 2 (3)(b)) gives details of the fire tests required for elements of structure and methods by which fire resistance is determined. Dependent on the function of the element, it has to satisfy one or more of the following criteria.

(i)   Stability ie. the ability of the specimen tested to withstand deformation or collapse.

(ii) Integrity ie. the ability to withstand cracking or opening up to the extent of allowing flames to pass through.

(iii) Insulation ie. the ability of the face of the element not exposed to heat to remain comparatively cool.

Large numbers of various types of elements of structure have been tested over a period of years. The designer of a building can, therefore, refer quite readily to previous test results from a range of official publications and will know whether, or not, the particular type of construction selected will be appropriate in respect to the fire resistance. Should the designer wish to use new or untested materials, testing would be necessary and a satisfactory report furnished to the proper authority prior to approval being given for the use of such elements in the construction of a particular building.

Reference has already been made, in the Introduction to Part 1, to the limitations of fire test results. In some aspects of fire testing the ability of a material, or structure, to pass a standard test may be only a minor consideration in the decision as to whether, or not, that material or structure will be safe or suitable for use.

This limitation, however, applies little to the testing for fire resistance as the ability of an element of structure to offer fire resistance is a relatively positive quality, applying in any circumstances in which that element of structure might be used.

9 Terminology

In approved Document B2 of the BR various terms dealing with elements of structure are defined and firefighters should consult this publication if they wish to learn the correct definitions. For simplicity of reference, the words "column" and "beam" in this Book have been used, throughout, to indicate, respectively, vertical and horizontal load-bearing members, irrespective of the materials from which they are made or the positions in which they are used.

Table 1 gives a list of the terms generally used by architects and builders so that firefighters may recognise them when reading other technical publications. Generally speaking the term "lintel" is now used for any beam spanning an opening although the term "bressumer" may still be occasionally employed to describe a larger span.

Table I

Material	When used as a column	When used as a beam
Stone	Pier, column or pillar	Lintel, arch
Brick	Pier or pilaster	Arch or flat arch
Timber	Post or strut	Joist, lintel, bearer, beam, rafter
Steel	Stanchion, strut or column, roof member, Universal steel section	Joist, universal steel section, beam, lintel, truss.
Wrought or cast iron	Column	Beam, girder, lintel
Reinforced concrete	Column	Beam, lintel

Chapter 4
True elements of structure

1 Fire resistance

The Building Regulations ADB3 Section 7. 1 states:-

Premature failure of the structure can be prevented by provisions for loadbearing elements of structure to have a minimum standard of fire resistance, in terms of resistance to collapse or failure of loadbearing capacity. The purpose is threefold:

(i) to minimise the risk to occupants some of whom may have to remain in the building for some time whilst evacuation proceeds, if the building is a large one;

(ii) to reduce the risk to firefighters who may be engaged on search or rescue operations;

(iii) to reduce the danger to people in the vicinity of the building who might be hurt by falling debris or as a result of the impact of the collapsing structure on other buildings.

Table A1 in Appendix A of the ADB lays out the specific provisions for the fire resistance of elements of structure. Table A2 gives the minimum periods of fire resistance for the different purpose groups of buildings

2 Columns

The function of a column is to carry part of the weight of the building where an internal wall would interfere with the designed use or where a large open space is needed. A column is often designed to withstand only vertical loads and any eccentric loading greatly increases the stress and will overturn any column not rigidly fixed at its foot. The 6 principal materials which have been used for the construction of columns are: Timber, brick, stone, reinforced and pre-stressed concrete, cast-iron and steel.

a. Timber.

At the beginning of the 19th century timber was normally used for columns in multi-storey factories and mills and some of these buildings still exist. Timber columns (Fig. 4.1) are usually found fitted with cast-iron caps which accommodate the ends of the wooden beams. When these columns are located one above the other, on various floors , a cast-iron pintle (a bar of round section) runs through the beam in line with the column and transmits the load. This avoids the undue crushing force on the intervening timberwork.

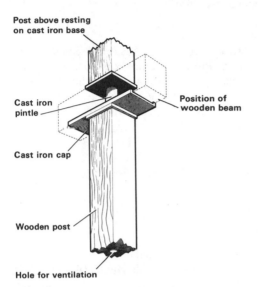

Post above resting on cast iron base

Cast iron pintle

Position of wooden beam

Cast iron cap

Wooden post

Hole for ventilation

Fig. 4.1 Sketch showing the construction of a typical timber post and of the cast-iron cap and pintle used to transmit the load through a floor.

b. Laminated timber

Techniques for laminating sections of timber are well established and usually replace the more costly baulks of timber. The sections are described as "glulam" and their designed load-carrying capacity can be accurately calculated as well as their fire-resistance.

c. Brick

Brick columns are usually found in basements supporting beams which, in turn, take the load of the building above. A development of brick column building are post-tensioned columns. These are stressed in a similar way to post-tensioned concrete and resist forces, which would tend to overturn the column, by compressing the column lengthways. These can be found in all areas of a building.

d. Stone

Stone columns in old buildings, even if particularly massive in appearance may not be as solid as they look. Some will have been constructed with facing stones filled behind with rubble and mortar. This rubble could have settled leaving the column load carried by the facing stones only. More modern columns may, or may not, be load-bearing but where they are they will most probably conceal steel stanchions behind a stone face. Firefighters should also be aware of the trend nowadays of erecting "stone" columns which are made of tough plastic or fibre-glass covering a steel girder.

e. Reinforced concrete

The reinforcing steelwork in structural concrete has developed to a very high standard (see Plate 3) today. Pre-cast factory constructed units are probably more in use on sites using modular building methods but a lot of steel fabrication is done on site and the concrete poured into formwork around the steel reinforcement. The fire resistance of a concrete column depends on:

(i) the applied load

(ii) the type and strength of the concrete

(iii) the dimensions of the column

(iv) the method of reinforcement

(v) its resistance to collapse.

A column should have at least the fire resistance of the elements of structure which it supports or carries and this, under the Building Regulations, depends on what type of structure they are a part. Obviously a higher standard of fire resistance will require greater dimensions and adequate protection of the steelwork.

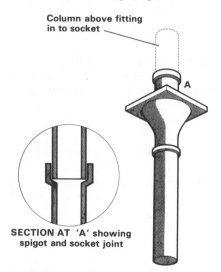

SECTION AT 'A' showing spigot and socket joint

Fig. 4.2 Sketch showing the construction of a cast-iron column and the method which is used to transmit the load through a floor.

f. Cast-iron

Although seldom used in modern buildings cast iron columns will be found in many old buildings and especially manufactories. There are numerous shapes and fittings and often different types will be found in the same building where extensions have been carried out. A common type is a circular tube with a rectangular capping which carries the ends of the beams. The height of the column is the same as that of the floor and can vary from 2.7m to 6m whilst diameters can be 450mm on the lowest floor of a large building to 150mm on the top floor of a small building. The bases of the columns on each floor fit into the caps of the columns below but are not, usually, bolted to them. Quite often a central spigot fits into a socket and these can be either of wood or metal (Fig. 4.2). It is not unusual to find cast-iron columns still standing after a fierce fire when the remainder of the building has collapsed (see the Manual, Book 11, Plate 12).

g. Structural steel

Steel columns are usually of I section rolled as a single piece. Occasionally, where necessary they may be strengthened by flat plates riveted to the flanges and they can run up through more than one floor. The horizontal joists carrying the various floors would then be bolted or riveted to the column. Structural steelwork has the disadvantage of being unable to withstand the high temperatures generated under fire conditions and it will quickly loose its strength, buckle and fail. It must, therefore, usually be protected where fire resistance is required and the type of protection can be either "solid" or "hollow".

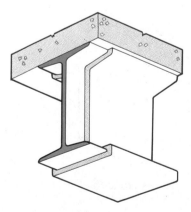

Typical beam encasement

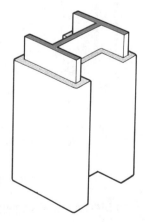

Typical column encasement

Fig. 4.3 Example of "solid protection" to a steel section beam and column.

(i) Solid protection

Nowadays this is achieved (a) by concrete encasement or (b) spraying with different types of mineral fibre vermiculite cements, magnesium oxychlorides etc. (Fig. 4.3 and Plate 1) or (c) application, either by spray or brush, of intumescent paints. The degree of fire resistance required in the case of (a) and (b) will depend on the density of the application and its thickness. The same applies in part to (c) although the chemical ingredients will dictate the amount of intumescing that takes place and also the protection afforded by the carbonaceous char.

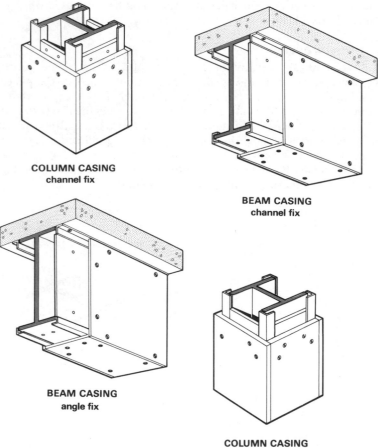

COLUMN CASING
channel fix

BEAM CASING
channel fix

BEAM CASING
angle fix

COLUMN CASING
angle fix

Fig. 4.4 Different types of hollow protection to beam and column.

(ii) Hollow protection

This is the encasement of steelwork by fire-resistant boards (Fig. 4.4) and the Building Regulations give guidance in the Approved

Document B. Again the materials from which the boards are made vary from manufacturer to manufacturer. Vermiculite is often used, sometimes combined with gypsum, but there are other ingredients. Modern boards have gone away from asbestos for health reasons but these will still be found and give good protection.

A method now used is covered mesh protection which combines fire resistant compounds sprayed onto a fire-resisting metal mesh surrounding the steelwork. A third method is to fill in the hollow protection with additional thermal protection – mineral fibre, fibre glass, rock-wool, foamed slag etc. All of which will add to the fire resistance of the steel. Needless to say most of these coverings should be finished off very carefully at joints, especially at floors and walls, to ensure that the whole is up to the required standard.

The fire resistance of the various methods of protection must be at least that laid down by the Building Regulations for that particular type of occupancy. In addition any column must have the fire resistance of not less than the period required for any element which it carries and, if it forms part of more than one building or compartment, must comply with the maximum fire resistance for those buildings or compartments. Heavy steel columns fail less readily than light ones as the thermal capacity ie. the ability to absorb heat, of the heavy column is greater for the same temperature rise. Consequently, a light steel column will require probably more protection than a heavy one.

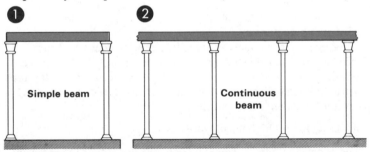

Fig. 4.5 Diagram showing two types of beam. (1) a simple beam, (2) a continuous beam.

3 Beams

The primary function of a structural beam is to support an applied load. A simple beam (Fig. 4.5(1)) is one of short span supported at each end. A continuous beam (Fig. 4.5(2)) is one used in longer spans and supported on a series of columns. In this way a greater load can be carried than by using a series of simple beams. When a load is applied to a beam it bends slightly ie. deflects the upper section being compressed and the lower section tending to stretch ie. be put under tension. An exaggerated diagram of this is shown in Fig. 4.6.

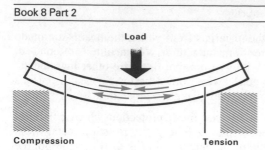

Load

Compression   Tension

Fig. 4.6 Diagram showing the effect of deflection on a beam. The curvature shown is greatly exaggerated.

a. Timber beams

Except in houses, solid timber is very seldom used in structural framing but could be found in the older industrial buildings. The charring rate of timber is generally accepted as 0.64mm per minute and an uncharred core is neither materially affected or significantly reduced in strength. Recently there has been a resurgence in the use of laminated (glulam) timber for public buildings. Spans of 150m are not uncommon using glulam made of European Whitewood (see Plate 23). The claimed charring rate for this glulam is 0.40mm per minute and the structural integrity is good because of the high fire resistance of the laminating adhesives. It is apparently possible to predict the inherent fire resistance of a component for a specified period and standards are set in BS 5268 Part 4. 1978. Class 0 surface spread of flame is usually obtained by the application of a proprietary treatment after the structure is erected.

b. Reinforced concrete

To compensate for its lack of tensile strength concrete beams are reinforced by high tensile steel rods. These are usually held in place by a designed system of steel lattice work (Plate 3) according to the type of construction strength required and then encased in concrete. Steel is used for reinforcement for 3 reasons :

(i) It can withstand high tensile stresses

(ii) The expansion rates of steel and concrete are almost the same and

(iii) the adhesion between the 2 surfaces in contact results in efficient bonding of the 2 materials

These beams are inherently non-combustible but the fire resistance is dependent on the cross-sectional area of the beam and the amount of concrete cover provided for the reinforcement. Although reinforced concrete is a good structural material, being very strong and capable of almost limitless fabrication and flexibility in design it has 2 main problems:

(1) The heavy deadload of the material results in limited effective spans of floors and beams unless specialist techniques are used.

(2) Due to the low elasticity of concrete and the high elasticity of steel, soffits of floors and beams may crack on overload and the steel, if not properly protected, may be attacked by the capillary action of moisture etc.

This is one of the reasons why, in order to overcome these problems, a system of pre-stressing concrete was introduced.

c. Pre-stressed concrete

This method depends on the reliability of control of the aggregate and mix proportions, the placing of the concrete, the quality of the steel reinforcing and the application of the precise degree of stress to the cables.

There are 2 methods of pre-stressing concrete:

(1) Pre-tensioning.

Here the cables are stretched between the anchor blocks fixed to the pre-stressing bed. The framework is then arranged around the cables and concrete case. When the concrete has matured sufficiently, the cables are released and, in trying to return to their own lengths, they compress the concrete (see Fig. 4.7).

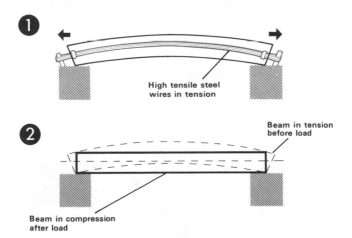

High tensile steel
wires in tension

Beam in tension
before load

Beam in compression
after load

Fig 4.7 Diagram showing pre-stressing of concrete beams. (1) Pre-compression induced in the 'fibres' where under working load tensile stresses would be expected. (2) When the load is applied, there remains in the normally 'tensile zone' sufficient compressive stress to neutralise the tensile stresses of the applied load.

(2) Post-tensioning.

The method used here is that the cables are stressed after the concrete is set and has reached an adequate strength. The cables, or bars, are anchored at one end of the members and, using a special jack, are stretched until the right stress is reached and then anchored at the other end. The whole idea is to induce the concrete in the "tensile region" to be in compression. When a load is applied there remains, in the normally "tensile zone", sufficient compressive strength to neutralise the tension. (see Fig. 4.8).

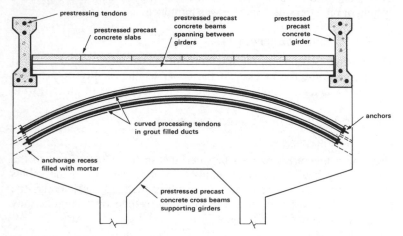

Fig. 4.8 A typical example of the structured use of prestressed concrete.

d. Cast-iron

Although beams are no longer made of cast-iron there are many which still exist. A feature of all cast-iron beams is a large bottom flange (Fig. 4.9), the top flange being smaller or, occasionally, omitted altogether. Stiffeners are cast on the web and the ends shaped to fit the head of the cast-iron; column to which they are bolted.

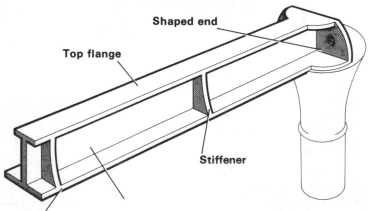

Fig. 4.9 A typical cast-iron beam.

e. Steel

Beams of structural steel are usually referred to by the function they are required to perform eg. main beam, tie beam, joist. The term "universal beam" is used to denote one of a range of sections usually of the same type but varying in size and mass per kilogram per metre run. Most beams are of a rolled "I" section with, if necessary, additional flats rivetted to the top and bottom flanges to give it added strength. Where fire resistance is required the same methods as specified for columns apply.

f. Steel lattice joists.

This type of beam consists of cold-rolled steel bars or tubes welded to top and bottom plates most of which are profiled for a particular reason eg. the type of decking shown in Fig. 4.10 which can be used as permanent shuttering for a reinforced concrete slab. These beams are light but strong, easily erected and ideal for lightweight roofs or floors and are found in large single and two-storey industrial storage and commercial buildings.

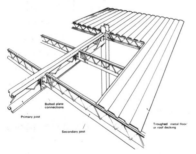

Fig. 4.10 Typical construction for joisted floor or roof.

g. Open-web beam – castella type.

As shown in Fig. 4.11 and Plate 2, this type of beam has been cut along a castellated line and then welded back together again. This increases the depth of the beam one and a half times and reduces the deflection under load. Both steel lattice joists and castellated beams are often used to support ceilings as their design allows all types of services to be run through the beams.

4 Walls (load-bearing)

As with steel, walls are usually referred to by the function they perform eg. external, compartment, separating, load-bearing. In the following paragraphs some of the types of loadbearing walls are described.

a. Solid brick

The commonest type of loadbearing wall, and one which is also widely

39

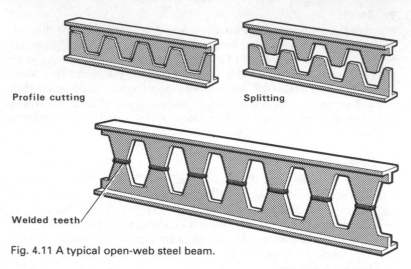

Profile cutting   Splitting

Welded teeth

Fig. 4.11 A typical open-web steel beam.

used as a non-loadbearing panel wall in a framed building, is made of brick. The nominal size of a brick, at least in the south of England, is 228 x 114 x 76mm and the thickness of a brick wall is measured in multiples of a half-brick ie. 114mm. Thus a "brick-and-a-half" wall, as shown in Fig. 4.12, is 342mm and a "half-brick" wall is 114mm thick. The bricks are bedded in mortar which may consist of a mixture of lime and sand with water (lime-mortar) or a lime mortar to which has been added a proportion of cement (lime cement mortar or "compo") or of a mortar consisting of cement, sand and water.

Lime mortar is relatively soft and may be protected on the outside of the building by "pointing" the joint with a stronger mortar.

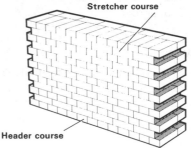

Stretcher course   Metal tie

Cavity

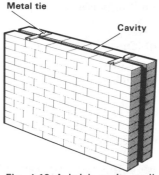

Header course

Fig. 4.12 A solid brick wall laid in English bond.

Fig. 4.13 A brick cavity wall, showing the metal ties and stretcher bond with, at the ends, snap headers

Bricks are arranged in a wall so that the vertical joints of one layer, or "course", do not coincide with the joints of the course below. This is known as "bonding" and a number of different arrangements or "bonds" are in general use. Shown in Fig. 4.12 is the strongest type and the most usual in the UK for thick walls. It is known as "English Bond". The cavity wall construction (Fig. 4.13) described in para. (b) below, is laid in "stretcher bond" with bricks laid lengthways with "snap headers" ie. bricks cut in half and laid with their ends on the face of the wall to give the necessary bond.

b. Cavity brick

Cavity walls are used mainly as external walls in buildings particularly exposed to weather. The object of the cavity is to prevent rain penetrating to the inside face of the wall. The usual type of cavity wall found in domestic buildings (Fig. 4.13) consists of two half-brick walls held together by metal ties and separated by a 50mm cavity. Sometimes the internal wall is only 76mm thick in modern buildings and is built either of bricks laid on edge or concrete slabs. Whatever method is used the weight of the upper floors, and sometimes the roof, is carried on this internal wall.

The cavity may, or may not, be ventilated to the outside air by air-bricks at the top and bottom. In modern building practice the cavity is sometimes filled with an inert material giving additional thermal insulation to the building.

Another type of construction which uses brick as the "outer skin" is that of modern timber-framed construction. Here the main structure is of timber with the frame clad internally and externally with building board usually of an insulating type. On the outside of this, with a small gap, is laid a conventional brick "skin". A membrane of either plastic or bitumenized paper is placed between the inner and outer skins. In order to prevent fire spread in the cavity a system of fire-stopping is placed at appropriate spots in the cavity. Even if construction is carried out to a good standard, firefighters may have to penetrate the inner skin to locate, and extinguish, a fire in the cavity. This type of construction is not limited to houses but may also be found in two-storey residential homes, hotels, schools etc. Methods of construction vary and firefighters should take any opportunity to inspect these types of buildings because they can present problems.

c. Timber-framed

It must be stressed that this type of timber framing is very different to that in the preceding paragraph, and is usually only found on very old buildings. The timbers here are infilled with brickwork, plaster, reeds and plaster (wattle and daub) and various other materials including flints and stones. Again, due to settlement, additions to the building over a long time, alterations internally, rodents etc. any fire can spread through numerous cavities and break out almost anywhere.

d. Other walls

There are numerous types of solid walls ranging from the old stone walls a meter thick to stone-fronted brick walls (Fig. 4.14). Other walls can consist of hollow blocks faced with stone slabs (Fig. 4.15) or concrete blocks built up in brick formations and rendered with plaster.

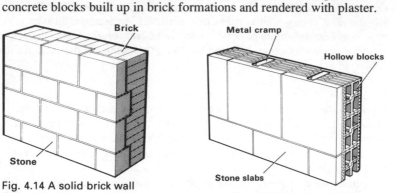

Fig. 4.14 A solid brick wall faced with stone.

Fig. 4.15 A hollow block wall faced with thin stone slabs.

e. Behaviour of loadbearing walls in fire.

The stability of a brick or stone wall depends, amongst other things on

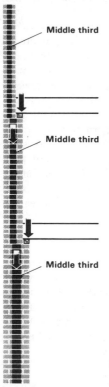

(i) its thickness in relation to its height

(ii) on proper bonding (in particular on the use of sufficient headers to tie the wall together)

(iii) to some extent on its age

(iv) on any horizontal pressure or levering effect which may exerted on it.

In a stone wall it also depends on the proportion of smaller stones which have been used and the skill of the builder. The fewer the number of joints and the thinner they are then the greater the strength of a stone wall.

A brick or stone wall, though capable of supporting a considerable vertical load, can only withstand a comparatively small sideways 'or lateral pressure and, for stability, the loading of a wall must be centred within the middle third (fig. 4.16). Provision is usually made in the design of the structure to withstand any normal lateral pressure, either by making the walls themselves thick enough for the purpose, or by the erection of transverse walls or buttresses. No provision is usually made for abnormal conditions such as may be brought about by fire. The expansion of steel joists may exert lateral pressure upon loadbearing

Fig. 4.16 Diagram (not to scale) showing how the load on a wall or column must be concentrated within the middle third.

walls into which they are fixed and expansion or other movement of the contents of a building may have a similar effect. Both these causes have been known to bring about the collapse of substantial brick walls.

A further frequent cause of collapse is uneven expansion. The heat-conductivity of brick or stone is low and it takes some time for heat to penetrate from one side of a wall to the other. The temperature of the surface of a brick wall in contact with a fire may, in consequence, be considerably higher then that of the farther surface and differences of as much as 500°C have been recorded in walls only one brick ie. 228mm thick. Since a rise in temperature causes expansion it is obvious that, if one surface of the wall is exposed to heat and expands whilst the other remains cool, the effect will be to bend the wall and throw it out of vertical and, in extreme cases, to cause its collapse.

In general, the collapse of walls has occurred at fires due to:

(i)　The burning away of the floors and crosswalls leaving a high wall with no side support.

(ii)　Expansion of beams built into the wall pushing it outwards, throwing it out of equilibrium.

(iii)　Disintegration of the joints. Lime and cement joints may be so weakened by the fire that a jet of water from a branch may be sufficient to throw the wall off balance and bring it down or to wash loose mortar out of the joints and destroy stability.

(iv)　The collapse of the support at the base of the wall such as an arch or a heavy steel beam. Provided there is no other damage to the wall, however, the bricks or stones may fall in such a way as to leave a natural arch over quite a large span and thus prevent total collapse. If this happens it is necessary to see that there is ample wall remaining on each side of the gap to support the load above and to resist spreading the "natural" arch.

(v)　heating and consequent expansion of the inside face of the wall throwing the wall outwards (see the Manual, Book 11 Plate 14).

(vi)　The levering action of collapsing joists which are built into the wall.

Experience in the collapse of stone walls in a fire tends to be contradictory. There have been cases of collapse in mill buildings in the north of England and many experienced fire brigade officers consider that, once a fire has obtained a substantial hold, collapse of some part of the structure is almost inevitable. In Scotland, on the other hand, where stone walls are almost universal, hardly any collapses have occurred and stone walls are, generally, considered as safe in almost any circumstances. The reason for this difference in behaviour may be the greater thickness and solidity of construction in Scotland or, possibly, in the type of stone used. Provided, however, that a stone wall is well built its fire resistance may be considered as substantially the same as that of a similar thickness of solid brick.

In a fire, a solid brick wall faced by stone behaves much the same as a solid brick or stone wall and there is little danger of the stone facing peeling off. On the other hand, when only a thin stone slab facing is used, often inadequately bonded to the wall, there is a danger of the slabs coming away from the wall as a result of a fire or explosion.

The wattle and daub wall is not fire resisting, but it is found, in practice, to delay the spread of fire and tends to smoulder rather than burn rapidly.

At the beginning of the last century many buildings were built with their walls covered externally with plaster or "stucco" as a cheap imitation of stonework. In this type of building the ornamental features, such as cornices, balconies, columns etc, may consist of stucco on wooden laths fixed to a wood framework. The wood is often extremely dry and the number of concealed spaces make firefighting difficult.

5. Floors

a. General

In all except single-storey buildings, floors are a principal structural element and vary greatly according to the design of the structure. In a steel-framed building the fame is designed to support the floor and, therefore, a designer can use pre-cast concrete slabs which will span between the joists (see Plate 4). In a reinforced concrete-frame building the whole frame and floors are usually pored in sequence to make a monolithic structure following which the shuttering is removed. A further development has come into use whereby the steel joists are spanned by light metal shuttering onto which a concrete floor is pored. The shuttering is left in place and becomes part of the floor. These are three examples of possible types of floor for, perhaps one office block design.

Floors can be regarded as being composed of 3 parts

(i)   the actual loadbearing members

(ii) the upper surface or finish of the floor and

(iii) the lower surface of ceiling of the compartment below.

In all but the most basic structures, where one construction combines all three, all three parts will be separate and identifiable.

For example, in a timber floor in a small house the loadbearing members are the joists, the surface is the boarding and the ceiling is of plaster. Here the preponderance of the strength of the combination is provided by the joists and, while the boarding adds to the rigidity, it is not an essential contributor; the plaster is itself supported by the joists.

Compare this with a reinforced concrete floor in which all three parts, ceiling, floor surface and structure may be completely merged. The whole thickness of the concrete slab contributes to the strength of the floor and the upper and lower surfaces provide the floor and the ceiling. This factor becomes more important when we come to consider membrane or suspended ceilings in compartmentation.

Construction of the more common types of floor is explained in the following paragraphs.

b. Timber floors

Timber floors will be found in many types of building and, in most cases, are required to provide certain levels of fire resistance according to the type and size of the building. Most timber floors are underdrawn with ceilings of various materials and these usually add considerably to the fire resistance. Other factors in the performance of timber floors in fire include:

(i) whether the flooring is plain edged (butted, tongued and grooved) or is chipboard or plywood

(ii) the thickness of the flooring

(iii) the loadbearing capacity of the joists (and the load imposed)

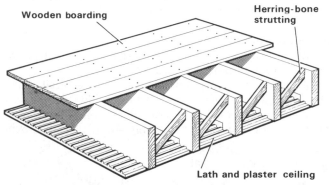

Wooden boarding

Herring-bone strutting

Lath and plaster ceiling

Fig. 4.17 A typical timber-joisted floor as used in domestic houses.

c. Timber-joisted floors

The timber-joisted floor (Fig. 4.17) has been generally used for the upper floors of houses of all periods. Butt-jointed or tongued and grooved boarding between about 16 and 32 mm thick is used, laid on wooden joists usually not less than 50mm thick and varying in depth from 128 to 180mm according to the distance spanned. These joists may be prevented from twisting by strutting, of which each unit may be either a solid board or two cross herring-bone struts, although nailed boards will have the same effect. On the underside of the joists is the ceiling usually, in modern work, of building board with a thin coat of plaster. This leaves a space between each joist enclosed by the floorboards and ceiling which constitutes hazard because fire can travel, undetected, in it. In the case of a hearth fire, in particular, it is often necessary to lift the floorboards at intervals to verify that the fire is not travelling to some other part of the structure.

45

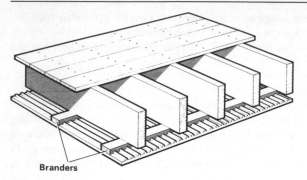

Branders

Fig. 4.18 Method of securing the ceiling laths to branders, sometimes used in Scotland.

In Scotland the laths or plasterboard are nailed to small battens called "branders" which run across the underside of the floor joists (Fig. 4.18). These branders prevent the joists from twisting but, since the laths or plasterboard are held away from the joists fire can spread through the small air-space more rapidly than in other types.

d. Floor supports at walls

The way that the joists are supported on the walls is of importance to the firefighter and several methods are used.

In old work the joists are simply built into the wall (Fig. 4.19(1) and there is a risk that the collapse of the joists in a fire could lever the wall off balance. A commoner method is the provision of a wood wall plate on to which the ends of the joists are nailed (Fig. 4.19(2)). This, if built

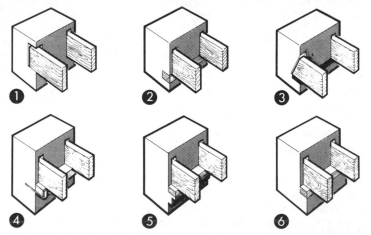

Fig. 4.19 Sketches showing various arrangements for supporting floor joists: (1) joist with square end in pocket; (2) joist carried on wooden wall plate; (3) joist with splayed end in pocket; (4) joist carried on wooden wall plate carried on bracket; (5) joist carried on wooden wall plate on corbelled brickwork; (6) joist carried on wooden wall plate on a ledge formed by reducing the thickness of the wall.

into a wall, tends to weaken it. A third method is to build in a wrought steel wall plate (Fig. 4.19(3)). Whichever design is adopted, unless sufficiently large "joist pockets" are allowed, collapsing joists will lever the wall off balance.

Of the more satisfactory methods used, from the point of view of fire, one is to support the wall plate on wrought-iron brackets built into the wall (Fig. 4.19(4)), a second is to corbel the brickwork out to form a ledge for the wood wall plate (Fig. 4.19(5) and a third is to reduce the thickness of the wall by 114mm at each floor level and to rest the wall plate on the ledge (Fig. 4.19(6)).

Many houses are floored with plywood or chipboard and this is laid in either one continuous sheet which could cover the whole of an upper floor or in large squares each about 900mm x 900mm. These are screwed to the joists and it is obvious that they present a problem to firefighters seeking to inspect joists or floor voids for fire damage or fire travel.

For many years ground floors of houses and similar constructions have been of concrete but this is changing back to the old style of suspended timber flooring. The ground floor is now frequently constructed in a similar manner to the upper floors and services will be run under them as elsewhere. Occasionally the void will be underdrawn with polystyrene sheets or filled with mineral wool for insulation purposes.

e. Brick arches

This is a type of construction mainly found in old warehouses, mills and manufactories and they may be supported on brick piers, cast-iron columns and beams and even, occasionally, on huge timbers. The upper surface is often filled in with concrete to make a level and boarded or screeded over.

f. Steel "filler" joists and mass concrete

There are many varieties of this type of floor but the principle employed is to divide up the area to be filled in by steel joists set at intervals sufficiently small to be spanned by mass ie. unreinforced, concrete.

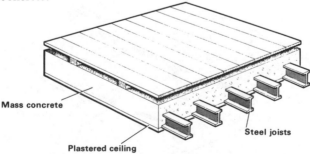

Fig. 4.20 Mass concrete and steel filler joist floor.

Two types of floor are illustrated in Figs. 4.20 and 4.21. In Fig. 4.20 light steel joists, 100 x 45mm, are placed 300mm apart and the space between and above filled in with 200mm of concrete. The top is finished off smooth and may be boarded, tiled etc. as required whilst the under side is usually plastered. This type has a very good fire record especially when supported on substantial brick walls.

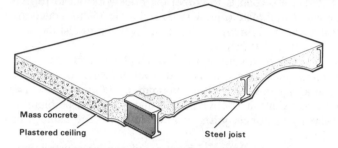

Fig. 4.21 Steel filler joist with arched construction mass concrete floor.

The second type (Fig, 4.21) the steel joists are heavier and spaced more widely and the concrete is arched up from the bottom flange of the joist to reduce the weight of the floor. The thickness of the concrete at the centre of the slabs may be as little as 75 to 100 mm and, in a fire, there is a danger of the slabs cracking away from the steel. In both types the lower flange of the steel joist may be entirely exposed to the full heat of any fire from below.

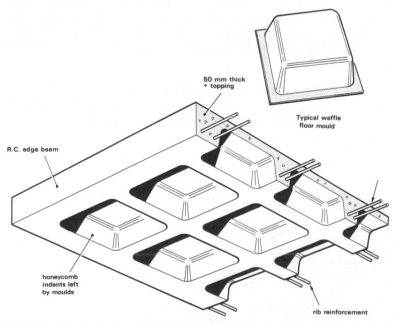

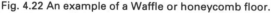

Fig. 4.22 An example of a Waffle or honeycomb floor.

g. Reinforced concrete (RC)

This type of flooring has developed from a fairly simple steel rod reinforcing to a highly sophisticated, interwoven steel mesh and rod combination onto which is poured a particular type of concrete and the strength and stresses on the whole can be very accurately calculated.

The actual under-configuration of the floor can be shaped by plastic or metal moulds (Fig. 4.22). These are sometimes called "waffle" or "honeycomb" floors and Plate 24 illustrates the combination of steelwork and glass fibre moulds required to formulate a floor of this kind.

Fig. 4.23 illustrates a sectional view of the type of reinforcing steel found in an RC beam.

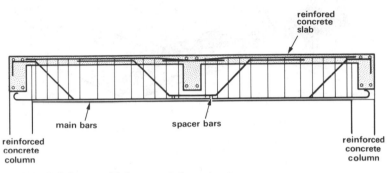

Fig. 4.23 R.C. beam with heavy reinforcement.

An older type is shown in Fig. 4.24. The construction is lighter and resembles the "waffle" type except that it has continuous arches. It is composed of RC beams spaced between 450 to 610mm apart with the spaces spanned by RC slabs structurally continuous with the beams. The actual thickness of the floor could be as little as 50mm and it is, therefore, inferior in fire resistance to the heavier RC type.

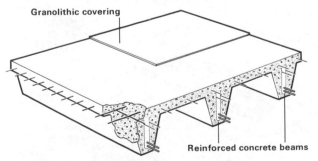

Fig. 4.24 Reinforced concrete rib and panel floor.

h. Pre-stressed concrete

Here pre-cast pre-stressed, either hollow or solid, concrete planks or sections are usually used to span between structural steel beams. After they are laid they are covered with concrete which bonds the planks together to make the finished solid floor. Two types are illustrated in Fig. 4.25 and Plate 4. Some are designed with in-built tie bars which help in the bonding when the concrete is overlaid.

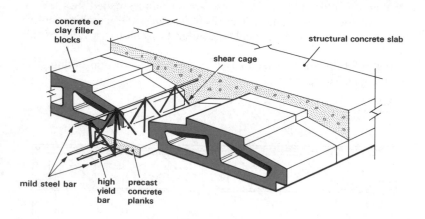

Typical composite floor using P.C.C. planks

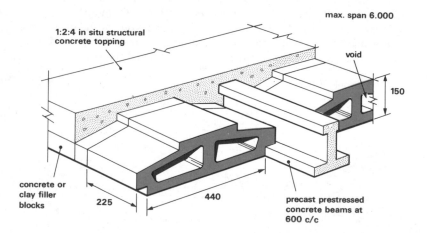

Typical composite floor using P.C.C. beams

Fig. 4.25 Two examples of plank floors overlaid with concrete.

i. Hollow block and plank

There are numerous variations of the types of concrete planks which can be quickly laid with spanning steel or concrete beams. Examples of these are shown in Fig. 4.26. Another lighter variation consists of hollow clay floor blocks held together in a light concrete topping with, or without, reinforcing steel, depending on the proposed loading on the whole floor (see Fig. 4.27).

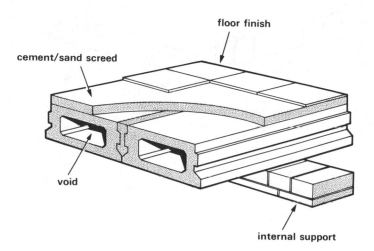

Typical hollow floor unit details

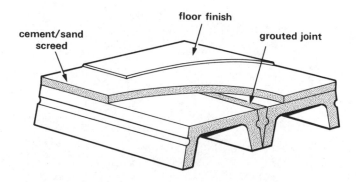

Typical channel section floor unit details

Fig. 4.26 Unreinforced plank floors with light concrete topping.

This type of floor has a good fire record although a fierce fire will tend to spall off the lower edge of the tiles. The remainder of the construction, however, is usually sufficient to maintain the stability of the floor.

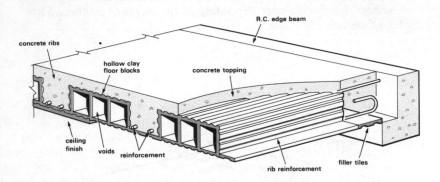

Fig. 4.27 A hollow clay block flow with reinforcement and a concrete topping.

Chapter 5
Other elements of structure

1 Non-load-bearing partition walls

The term "partition" or "partition wall" is used when referring to walls whose sole function is the division of a space within a building into separate rooms. In this section the term "partition" is used in the "space division" sense. These partitions are designed and constructed to carry their own weight and any fixture and fittings included in them ie. doors or glazing. They should also be robust enough mechanically for normal conditions of use, for example, able to resist vibration set up by doors being opened and slammed.

Partition walls are made from a variety of materials. Plasterboard bonded on either side of a strong cellular core to form rigid panels are suitable as non-load-bearing partitions. Compressed strawboard panels provide another alternative method and partially prefabricated partitions such as plasterboard and strawboard can be erected on site.

Non-load-bearing partitions often have quite good sound insulation qualities and will provide a certain period of fire resistance. For example, the fire resistance of timber-framed nonload-bearing partitions will be determined as much as anything by their lining/finishes. Plasterboard linings have an established resistance dependent upon the thickness applied. Plywood and chipboard linings of appropriate thickness also make a contribution to fire resistance.

a. Demountable partitions

In certain types of buildings it is often desirable to provide partitioning in a form which can be dismantled and re-erected easily to allow its use in another position. These demountable partitions are usually made up of fairly large components. Steel units or sheet materials such as plasterboard, strawboard and plastic-faced boards are frequently used; connections and angles formed by metal sections are sometimes of extruded light alloy frames (see Plate 5).

Firefighters need to be aware that some buildings with this type of partitioning can have their whole internal layout altered without prior notice being given.

2 Stairways

Prior to the introduction of the Building Regulations there was little, if any, control over the construction of stairs and badly designed stairs were fraught with danger in normal use let alone in fire and smoky conditions. The Regulations recognised this and now specify precise minimum dimensions for stairways in dwellings. Also the need to make buildings accessible to disabled people has resulted in ramps and these also come under the control of the Regulations.

In defining the minimum requirement for the safety of persons using a stairway, the Regulations differentiate between those for common use –

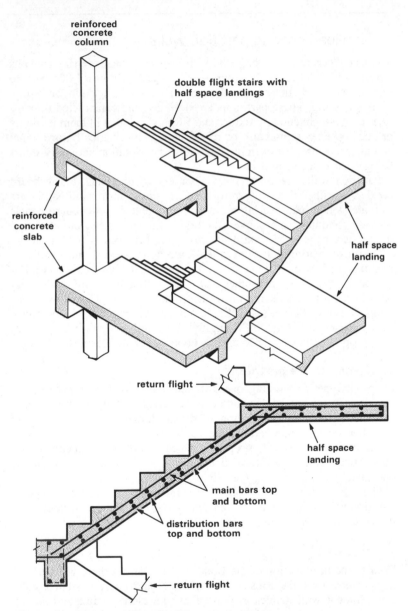

Fig. 5.1 Cranked or continuous slab concrete stairs.

stairways which serve two or more dwellings, and one dwelling. In all cases stairways and ramps which form part of the structure of the building are required to provide a safe passage for users. In many cases they may represent the only way out of the building in the event of a fire.

The requirements are, therefore, that they should be made from materials of limited combustibility and be continuous leading, ultimately, to a place of safety. This applies whether the stairway is internal or external. A provision is made that combustible material may be added to the upper surfaces of a stairway so that the use of carpets etc. is not precluded.

As a stairway is not designated an " element of structure" it is not required to have any fire resistance but, as stated above, must in most cases be made of materials of limited combustibility. This leaves a wide range of materials including solid timber and unprotected metalwork.

However, apart from private dwellings and some other residential premises, a good many buildings where either the public or considerable numbers of people resort, have stairways of stone, concrete or substantial metalwork. An example of a concrete slab stairway is shown in Fig. 5.1.

3 Doors and shutters

Doors and shutters are of seven principle types:

(a) Hinged doors

(b) Swing doors

(c) Revolving doors

(d) Sliding doors.

(e) Folding doors

(f) Cantilever doors

(g) Roller shutters.

In many gates and doors of industrial premises, a small door, often referred to as a 'wicket door', may be inset, eg. a hinged door set in a sliding gate.

a. Hinged doors

Hinged doors closing against a rebate on the door jamb are by far the most common. Types of hinged door are;

(1) Flush

Probably the commonest type of hinged door, and one which is relatively cheap to construct, is the lightweight flush door. This usually consists of two layers of plywood or hardboard with a honeycomb paper core. Sometimes the core is merely strips of strawboard glued on. The hollow door may be strengthened by a number of cross members; alternatively, some better types of flush door are solid.

(2) Panelled

Panelled doors usually have a wooden frame with wooden, or sometimes in the upper half, glass panels. There may be, in all, four panels, two small and two large.

(3) Ledged

Many ledged doors are of light construction. They may be ledged only or there may be bracing in addition or framing – a common type is framed, ledged and braced.

(4) Metal

Examples of steel-covered doors are shown in (Fig. 5.2 (1 & 2). Doors of this kind may sometimes be steel with wooden linings, so that the steel is concealed. Barred doors vary greatly in construction, but a typical example is shown in Fig. 5.2(3).

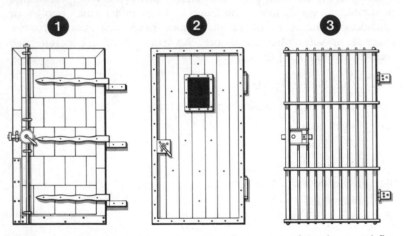

Fig. 5.2 Typical metal doors: (1) and (2). Two types of steel-covered fire-resisting door. (3) Barred door.

b. Swing doors

Any of the above types of door may be found with special pin hinges allowing them to swing in either direction, and consequently there is no rebate on the jamb. Such doors may consist of a single or a double leaf in a single opening. Swing doors are frequently uses in restaurants, hotels and department stores, and also on staircases and in long corridors to check the spread of smoke in case of fire. They are often partly glazed, the glass being wired or set in copper glazing bars (see 'copperlight glazing', Chapter 1), in those instances where some degree of fire resistance is required. If solid, they frequently have a glass panel and are generally of flush construction. In large department stores and modern office blocks, frameless swing doors of toughened glass may be encountered.

c. Revolving doors

Revolving doors present an obstruction to the firefighter since, unless they are first collapsed or broken in, they do not permit the passage of bulky objects or lines of hose. Revolving doors turn on central pivots at the top and bottom and usually have four wings arranged at right angles to one another. In some types of door only two wings may be found, each of which has a curved extension piece. The wings on the doors are generally constructed to collapse and to move to one side so as to give a relatively unobstructed opening. It is essential that this type of door is used in conjunction with a normal hinged door.

There are two common methods of securing the wings of revolving doors. In the first, the wings are usually held in place by a bracket or solid stretcher bar situated usually at the top of the door across the angle formed by the leaves where they join the newel post. One end of each bar is permanently connected to one leaf of the door and the other engages with some form of catch on the adjacent leaf. The wings are collapsed by releasing the stretcher bars, either by undoing the wing nuts or by unfastening the catches which hold them in place.

In the second type, the two opposing wings are hinged to the single leaf formed by the other two and are kept in position by a chain which runs through them and is held by a catch on each of the hinged leaves. If this catch is released, the wings can be folded back to give a clear opening.

d. Sliding doors

These doors may be either of solid construction or in the form of a lattice which collapses into a relatively small space when opened. Sliding doors may run on tracks above and below the door or be suspended from an overhead track. They are not often encountered in domestic property except possibly in garages, but those of solid construction are widely used in commercial premises, especially as fire-resisting doors for isolating sections of a building. These doors may either slide on one or both sides of the opening, or alternatively may move into a central recess in the wall.

Steel lattice doors are widely used to protect property where weather proofing in unimportant. The gate usually runs on two sets of tracks, one above and the other beneath, but may sometimes be found with a bottom track only. They are often to be found as a protection to the opening of a lift or lift shaft.

e. Folding doors

Folding doors are usually of fairly light construction, but exceptionally, they may be very large and of robust construction. They are often found as separating doors between two rooms where space is valuable. They are similar in design to normal hinged doors, but the two or more leaves are hinged together so that the whole door opens to one side only.

f. Cantilever doors

This door is counterbalanced and pivoted so that the whole door rises upwards and, when open, lies horizontally. Cantilever doors are usually found on garages, but steelplated doors of this type are also found in boiler houses. These doors generally fit flush in the opening.

g. Roller shutters

Roller shutters are nearly always made of steel, but may be constructed of timber. Small roller shutters can be raised by hand, but the larger sizes are almost invariably operated by means of gearing and some form of handle or chain and block on the inside.

4 Fire resistance of doors

a. Definition

Apart from its normal function, a standard door will (1) serve to contain an outbreak of fire and (2) will prevent the penetration of toxic smoke and fumes into otherwise unaffected parts of the building for a short period of time. A closed door also restricts the flow of oxygen thereby helping to starve the fire. It is for these reasons that all doors should be kept shut, particularly when a building is unoccupied for any length of time or at night. To be given a fire resistance rating, a complete doorset must be specially designed and built. Published Document 6512: Part 1:1985 defines a fire door as:

> "A door or shutter provided for the passage of persons, air or things which, together with its frame and furniture as installed in a building, is intended, when closed, to resist the passage of fire and/or gaseous products of combustion and is capable of meeting specified performance criteria to those ends".

b. Function of fire doors

Fire doors have at least two functions:

(1) to protect escape routes from the effects of fire so that occupants can safely reach a final exit:

(2) to protect the contents and/or the structure of a building by limiting the spread of fire.

Consequently a particular fire door may have to perform one or both of these functions for the purposes of smoke control, protecting means of escape, compartmentation or the segregation of special risk areas.

Fire doors provided for smoke control purposes are designed to restrict smoke movement and should be capable of withstanding:

(i) smoke at ambient temperatures and

(ii) limited smoke at medium temperatures:

Smoke control fire doors are provided for life safety purposes and play an important role in the vicinity of the fire in its early stages and in protecting escape routes more remote from a fully developed fire. There is, at present, no criteria for smoke control doors although a recommendation for performance for fire doors to resist the passage of smoke is under consideration. Opinion expressed in PD 6512:Part 1 is that smoke control doors should not, in the early stages of a fire, depend on either rebated door frames or heat activated seals, ie. intumescent strips. In practice doors are likely to warp and make rebates ineffective and heat activated seals which operate between 140°C and 300°C respond too late for the protection of escape routes from smoke.

Fire doors provided to protect means of escape should:

(i)   be capable of achieving a minimum fire resistance for integrity of only 20 minutes;

(ii) withstand smoke at ambient temperatures;

(iii) withstand limited smoke at medium temperatures.

These types of doors are required to keep escape routes sufficiently free from smoke for a sufficient time for occupants to reach a place of safety and to maintain integrity against the effects of fire for long enough to fulfil that objective. It follows that, in addition to smoke control capability, these doors require a measure of fire resistance. Consequently Codes of Practice generally recommend such doors to be either 20 or 30 minutes fire resistance and to have both flexible edge seals and heat activated seals ie. intumescent strips.

Doors for compartmentation and segregation of special risks are doors which must be capable of achieving the period of fire resistance appropriate to the structure which is not less than 30 minutes and may be as much as 4 or even 6 hours in exceptional circumstances. The required fire resistance may need to be achieved by the provision of two fire doors in series, both having half the required fire resistance. If such doors are required to protect an escape route they will need also to have the smoke control capabilities described above.

c. Identification of fire doors (see Table 3)

Fire doors should be identified by the initials FD followed by the performance in minutes that the door should achieve when tested for integrity only. For example a door identified as FD30 implies an integrity of not less than 30 minutes ie. 30 minutes fire resistance.

Where the door should also resist the passage of smoke at ambient temperatures the suffix 'S' should be added to the identification.

The practical application of the above is, for example, when specifying for a flat entrance door in a block of flats where the door would be required to protect a means of escape (see above) the requirement would be for a FD30S door. Or, alternatively, a fire door

Table 3 Provisions for fire doors

Position of door	Minimum fire resistance of door in terms of integrity (minutes)[1]
1. In a compartment wall separating buildings	As for the wall in which door is fitted, but a minimum of 60
2. In a compartment wall: a. if it separates a flat or maisonette from a space in common use.	FD 30S
b. enclosing a protected shaft forming a stairway situated wholly or partly above the adjoining ground in a building used for Flats, Other Residential, Assembly & Recreation, or Office purposes,	FD 30S
c. enclosing a protected shaft forming a stairway not described in (b) above,	Half the period of fire resistance of the wall in which it is fitted but 30 minimum and with suffix S
d. not described in (a), (b) or (c) above.	As for the wall it is fitted in, but add S if the door is used for progressive horizontal evacuation under guidance to B1
3. In a compartment floor	As for the floor in which it is fitted
4. Forming part of the enclosures of: a. a protected stairway (except where described in item 9),	FD 30S
b. lift shaft, or	FD 30
c. service shaft, which does not form a protected shaft in 2(c) above	FD 30
5. Forming part of the enclosures of: a. a protected lobby approach (or protected corridor) to a stairway	FD 30S
b. any other protected corridor	FD 20S
6. Affording access to an external escape route	FD 30
7. Sub-dividing: a. corridors connecting alternative exits,	FD 20S
b. dead-end portions of corridors from the remainder of the corridor	FD 20S
8. Any door: a. within a cavity barrier,	FD 30
b. between a dwellinghouse and a garage,	FD 30
c. forming part of the enclosure to a communal area in sheltered housing.	FD 30S
9. Any door: a. forming part of the enclosures to a protected stairway in a single family dwellinghouse,	FD 20
b. forming part of the enclosure to a protected entrance hall or protected landing in a flat or maisonette,	FD 20
c. within any other fire resisting construction in a dwelling not described elsewhere in this table.	FD 20

Notes
1. To BS476: Part 22 (or BS476: Part 8 subject to paragraph A5).

S   Unless pressurization techniques complying with BS 5588: Part 4 are used, these doors should also have a leakage rate not exceeding 3m³/m/hour (head and jambs only) when tested at 25 Pa under BS476: Section 31.1.

required in a compartment wall of 60 minutes fire resistance, with no means of escape implication, would have to be an FD60 door.

d. General

The fit of a door in its frame is a significant factor. The door stop of a 60 minute door is required to be cut from the solid timber frame whereas, in a 30 minute door, it is permissible for the stop to be screwed onto the frame. The weak point of a door in a fire is often the face on which the hinges are exposed and particularly the hinge side. It is important that hinges are made of noncombustible material and they are required to have a high melting point (800°C). PD 6512 states that, except where otherwise permitted, all fire doors should be provided with automatic self-closing devices. Where unlatched doors are used for smoke control purposes the selection of the self-closing device is critical. When other methods of smoke control are provided eg. pressurisation, the smoke control criteria for doors may not be applicable. It must not, however, be assumed that all doors must be fire-resisting. For example, it would be futile to require a door to be of a fire-resisting standard where the partition in which it is fitted is not required to perform any smoke or fire retardant function but is simply a convenient subdivision of space.

5 Windows

Windows allow natural light into buildings and also serve to ventilate rooms. Window frames can be made from a variety of materials such as timber, UPVC and metals like aluminium and steel. Windows can also be designed to operate in various ways by arranging for the sashes (the opening portion of the window including glass and frame) to slide, pivot or swing, by being hung on to one of the frame members.) Windows are generally referred to as being of two types according to the method of opening, these being "casement" or "sash".

a. Casement windows

The simplest consists of a square or rectangular window frame of timber or metal with the window casement hung ie. hinged at one side. When more than one casement is openable it is usual to refer to them as being 2, 3 or 4-1ight casements. Often a 2, or more, light casement window is in the form of ventlights. These are top-hung to open outwards. The horizontal framing between the casement and the ventlight is called the transom. Some windows of this type are constructed so that only part is openable. That part of the window which does not open is called a deadlight (see Fig. 5.3)

b. Sash windows

(1) Pivoted sash windows

The opening part of this type of window is supported by pivots at each side, or at the top and bottom, of the frame so that they open partly into,

Fig. 5.3 Casement windows: (1) single-light casement windows; (2) two-light casement with vent lights.

and partly out of, the room. The word sash describes the opening portion of a window and includes the glass and surround (see Fig. 5.4).

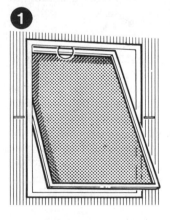

Horizontal – centre hung

Vertical – centre hung

Fig. 5.4 Pivoted sash windows: (1) pivots at each side. (2) Pivoted at the top and bottom. Note: O denotes usual position of catch.

(2) Sliding sash windows

The vertical sliding sash window with a double hung sash is the most commonly used type of sliding sash window and is constructed so that the two sashes slide vertically in the frame. Another type of sliding sash window consists of a frame in which there are at least two sashes, one or both of which can be opened horizontally (see Fig. 5.5).

Fig. 5.5 Sliding sash windows. (1) Double-hung vertically sliding sash window. (2) Horizontal sliding sash window.

c. Double-glazed windows

One sheet of glass in a window is a poor insulator against the transfer of heat. In order to reduce heat loss 2 sheets of glass, at least 5mm apart, are fixed in the casement or sash with clean dry air trapped between them and often hermetically sealed (see Fig. 5.6). Double-glazing does not increase the fire resistance of the glazing to any significant extent and, in fact, this type of glazing can shatter with explosive force when involved in fire.

Another arrangement consists of 2 separate windows, one on the outside opening out and one on the inside opening in. This also serves to reduce heat loss and sound penetration.

In may instances double glazed units contain toughened glass (this is particularly so where large sheets of glass are used). Firefighters should be aware that not only is it virtually impossible for the inhabitants to break this type of window in an attempt to escape but special means need to be employed to break in.

A new glazing concept now used takes full advantage of solar heat. A permanently sealed wafer-thin layer of silver plus other protective coatings give reflective quality with triple glazing efficiency. Other types of glazing are being developed which are not only energy efficient but also minimise air and water penetration and resist the effects of dust, dirt and solvents.

d. Triple glazing

Triple glazing is an extension of double glazing and is simply the addition of a third sheet of glass giving extra sound and heat insulation.

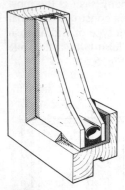

Fig. 5.6 Cut-away view of a double glazing unit.

e. Leaded windows

Leaded windows consist of a number of small panes of glass held together by strip lead. Such windows, especially those of coloured glass to be found in churches and cathedrals, may be of considerable value. The value lies in the glass not in the leading which can be replaced. The leaded panes are often held in position by light gauge bars running from side to side of the opening.

f. French windows

French windows are not, strictly speaking, windows but should be regarded either as a pair of panel doors or as casement windows.

6 Rooflights

A rooflight is a form of window in the plane of a roof and fixed. An opening rooflight is referred to as a 'skylight'. Rooflights are placed in buildings primarily to allow natural light in, some are fitted with louvered panels for ventilation. Many conventional rooflights still exist for example; Lantern lights: which consists of vertical glazed sides and a glazed roof – the sides are often arranged to open or are fitted with louvers for ventilation.

a. Monitor lights

These take the form of glass 'boxes' each with a flat top on flat or low-pitched roofs – the sides are usually arranged to open as with a lantern light.

b. Thermoplastics

More modern roof lights have been developed using thermoplastics. These include such materials as wire-reinforced pvc, anti-vandal polycarbonate and glass-reinforced polyester resin whilst others offer low-flammability or antiglare qualities. The use of plastic can be very economical and highly versatile with a variety of designs.

c. Traditional.

Traditional rooflights are still framed in metal. Aluminium is mostly used because of its low cost. The glazing in these and almost all rooflights is 6mm wired glass. In the event of a fire, this does reduces the risk of glass falling onto persons below, however, it also delays the venting of a fire as the design ensures that the glass is held together and initially will only crack in fire conditions. To prevent natural heat losses through the roof, some systems employ double glazing; these systems will also delay the venting of a fire within.

d. Venting

Some rooflights are intended to form a vent when destroyed by heat ie. roof ventilators in the form of haystack lantern lights installed above the stage area of theatres. Hazardous conditions can arise however if a rooflight is recessed above a soffit or a suspended ceiling where a fire can develop undetected. Alternatively, heat and flame escaping from a rooflight may reach an adjacent building or flammable materials if it is not well placed. The exposure hazard thus created must be covered in firefighting operations.

It is important to remember however that most rooflights will fail in heat. Smoke, heat and flames can be vented to the outside air thereby ensuring that firefighting can commence in more favourable conditions.

7 Hearths, flues and chimneys

a. General

The word 'chimney' is used to include the structure from the hearth to the external smoke outlet, the smoke route itself is a flue. Around 1844, local authorities were given power to control building and set standards and these included quite stringent requirements for hearths. At the present time the Building Regulations specify the methods of construction of hearths, chimneys and flues. The regulations are quite complex and it would be inappropriate to attempt to explain them in detail. In essence, the Regulations require:

> "Any chimney, flue-pipe, constructional hearth or fireplace recess to be constructed of materials of limited combustibility and of such a nature, quality and thickness as not to be unduly affected by heat, condensation and products of combustion; also to be so constructed and of such thickness, or in the case of flue-pipe, so placed, as to prevent the ignition of any part of the building".

b. Hearth fires

Many hearth fires which occurred in those built prior to byelaws and regulations were often the result of poor construction or general wear and tear. Most commonly, cracked hearths led to spalling of the brickwork and penetration of sparks and embers. Many were the result of work carried out by the D. I. Y enthusiast who effected changes without being aware of the necessary precautions which needed to be taken. However, these type of hearths are no longer built and any existing ones should have been replaced with the advent of the Building Regulations.

c. Chimneys

Chimney fires were quite common and were often the result of bad design or the infrequency with which they were swept – this would lead to a gradual build-up of soot which would eventually catch alight. Todays modern heating systems still require a balanced flue but the linings tend to be made from aluminium. Those still constructed for traditional fireplaces are made from pre-cast concrete pipes of several metres in length enabling designers to build the conventional vertical chimney either boxed in or disguised in some fashion. The Manual, Book 11, Chapter 5 gives information on how to tackle chimney and hearth fires.

8 Roofs

a. General

It has been stated that "a roof is a structure which surmounts a building to keep out the weather and may be flat, pitched or curved". Whether this could be applied to some modern buildings with roofs made of fabric, glass, plastics, tubing, cables etc. and which are suspended, cantilevered, sometimes geodetic, frequently braced and, occasionally, inflated is problematical. Many single-storey industrial buildings appear to carry the walls straight over into the roof and consist of polymerised insulation sandwiched between metal cladding. Others include large areas of glass or polycarbonate which, again, covers both walls and roof. This section will, however, describe some of the

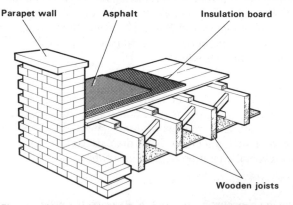

Parapet wall   Asphalt   Insulation board

Wooden joists

Fig. 5.7 Wooden-joisted flat roof with parapet. For simplicity details of the damp courses have been omitted from the parapet wall.

commonest and simplest types of roof but emphasises the need for firefighters to note the construction of new types of roof in their areas.

b. Flat roofs

The construction of flat roofs varies from what is little more than a weatherproofed floor to a concrete plank assembly which is, itself, weatherproofed by screeding, grouting and bitumenising. Fig. 5.7 shows a traditional construction like an upper floor, covered in a fibreboard and bituminised felt or poured asphalt. Fig. 5.8 illustrates a floor of reinforced concrete with a bituminised weatherproofing and heat insulating tiles. Both are common basic constructions and the variety is endless.

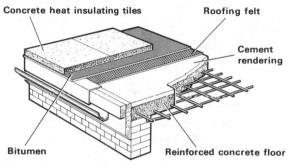

Concrete heat insulating tiles   Roofing felt

Cement rendering

Bitumen   Reinforced concrete floor

Fig. 5.8 Concrete flat roof without parapet.

c. Pitched roofs

Probably the most common type of roof used in 90% of houses and residential accommodation is the pitched roof.

(1) Close-coupled roofs

The simplest and most common form of pitched roof is called a close-coupled roof. Timber rafters about 300mm apart run from a ridge-board to a wall plate on the top of an external wall at eaves level. These rafters carry the sloping roof which can be of various materials. Where rafters are longer than about 2m they require support in the middle (Fig. 5.9). This is done by a timber called a purlin which supports the centres of all the rafters and, on long spans, is itself supported by timber struts placed at intervals on the tops of internal walls. On every large close-coupled roofs there may be two purlins under each slope.

The ceiling joists are nailed to the wallplate and to the rafters (metal connectors may be used, see chapter 11 section 2 and Fig. 5.10) so that the whole construction forms a series of triangles which resist the tendency for the roof to spread outwards (see Fig. 5.11). Occasionally the two sets of rafters are also connected together at about half the height of the roof by transverse timbers called collars. These help to stiffen the roof by reducing the free span of the rafters. The rafters may continue beyond the line of the wall and overhang to form the eaves. Horizontal

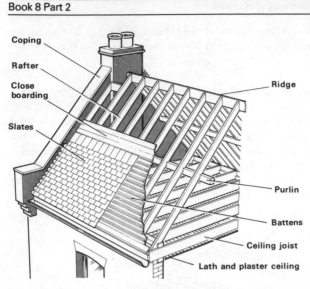

Coping
Rafter
Close boarding
Slates
Ridge
Purlin
Battens
Ceiling joist
Lath and plaster ceiling

Fig. 5.9 Sketch showing the more important features of the form of roof construction often used in domestic dwellings.

boarding may often be used below the eaves to keep out draughts, birds etc. from the roof space. In addition the spaces between the rafters should be filled with bricks to roof level but this is not often done.

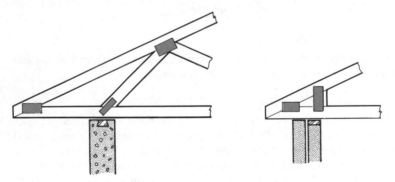

Fig. 5.10 An illustration of low metal connectors are used to join roof members.

This type of construction is mostly used in houses as well as for great numbers of other small buildings and there are several variations. For instance, the ceiling joists may be set up above the level of the top of the walls so that the rafters form part of the ceiling in the room below. This is known as a "camp roof". Again, it may be found that rooms have been formed in the roof space if it is high enough by means of vertical framing (see Fig. 5.12) the whole being lined with some sort of wallboard. The framing thus forms vertical walls to he rooms and there is some sloping ceiling on the underside of the rafters and a horizontal portion on the underside of the collars.

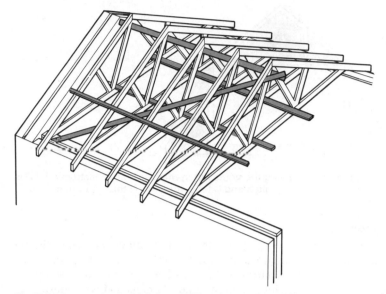

Fig. 5.11 One method of joining and bracing roof members.

(2) Mansard roofs

A mansard roof is a special type of pitched roof and instead of the roof running up at a constant angle from eaves to ridge there are two angles. One is a very steep pitch from the eaves to room height (Fig. 5.13(1)) and then a flatter pitch above (Fig. 5.13(2)). The object of this is to enable a room to be built inside the roof space which, in effect, becomes another storey.

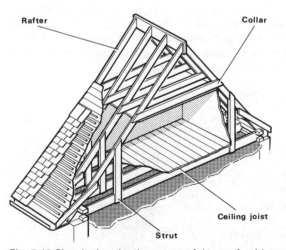

Fig. 5.12 Sketch showing how part of the roof void may be utilised to form a room.

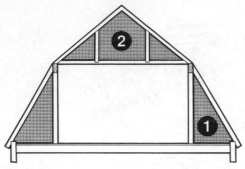

Fig. 5.13 Diagram showing the voids left in mansard roof construction: (1) is the void left by the steep pitch and (2) the void left by the flatter pitch.

d. Trussed roofs

This type of roof is used to spread the load and direct it to the walls and the ground. Construction varies widely both in its use and design. The older styles of timber rafters, either tensioned by iron rods or timber, and the cast-iron trussing found in large old mills and warehouses etc. have been superseded by laminated timber, steel tubing, steel lattice girders and aluminium. The large spans over concert halls theatres and cinemas are types of trussed roof as are the ultra modern tubular steel and geodetic fabrications in shopping centres and other large enclosed areas etc.

e. The Portal or rigid frame roof

The Portal frame consists of, essentially, a continuous member conforming to the outline of the roof and connected to vertical columns. This continuous frame has the effect of passing the roof loading to the rest of the structure (Fig. 5.14). They are especially suitable for single storey industrial or storage buildings giving long, wide open areas. Steel, aluminium and laminated timber are used but most are of precast prestressed concrete units.

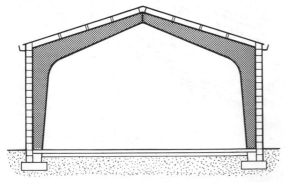

Fig. 5.14 Typical Portal or rigid frame roof construction.

f. Monitor roof

A type of roof found in factories or stores is illustrated in Fig. 5.15. It is of a relatively light weight and is designed to give the maximum amount of light by the use of "upstands" of glass or polycarbonate. The nonglazed portions are usually light decking and the walls are generally of a lightweight "sandwich" cladding, the whole supported by precast concrete frames.

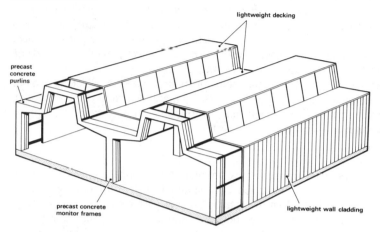

Fig. 5.15 Typical monitor roof profiles.

g. Roofing materials

(1) Slates and tiles

The simplest form of pitched roof covering consists of slates or tiles nailed or laid on wooden battens which are, themselves, nailed to the rafters. Felt is sometimes laid under the battens for the purpose of heat insulation or weatherproofing. In better quality work, boarding and felting may be employed the tiling battens being nailed through them to the rafters below. Slates may be thin and comparatively light in weight or they may be thick and heavy. All slates must be nailed on.

Plain tiles are flat or slightly curved on both sides and have "nibs" at the top which are used to hook them onto the battens. Tiles rest in position by their own weight and in only the best work are they secured by rails to the battens. Pantiles are heavier and curly in shape and are hooked on in most cases. Concrete tiles will also be found to resemble both the interlocking and the plain clay tiles.

To prevent entry of rain, especially where there is a heavy weather exposure, slates and tiles may be bedded in mortar. This is a process known as "torching".

Tiles can also be found made of asbestos-cement and were extensively used in bungalows, sports pavilions and other inexpensive structures. They can be distinguished by the considerably larger area covered by each tile and, owing to their light weight, should require less heavy roof timbers.

(2) Sheeting

Corrugated iron, aluminium and corrugated asbestos sheet require a different form of roof construction because the large sheets of material are fixed to purlins not battens. With these materials no common rafters are used. The principal rafters (or trusses in large buildings) are widely spaced – as much as 2 - 3.5m apart in the case of principal rafters and 3-5m in the case of trusses – and themselves support the purlins. There is a line of purlins to each row of corrugated sheet placed under the line where the sheets lap over one another.

Roofs of corrugated iron and corrugated asbestos-sheet have poor insulation and are often underdrawn by matchboarding or plasterboard. They will take little weight and firefighters must exercise the utmost caution when working on or near them.

(3) Cladding

Nowadays many single-storey industrial buildings are clad in metal sheeting which is corrugated but usually in square or oblong section. As stated before, often the roof is all one part with the wall (see Fig. 5.16) and consists of a polyisocyanurate or polyurethane foam insulation sandwiched between two sheets of steel sheeting or an aluminium-alloy sheeting. These are fixed to metal rails along the walls and metal purlins in the roof.

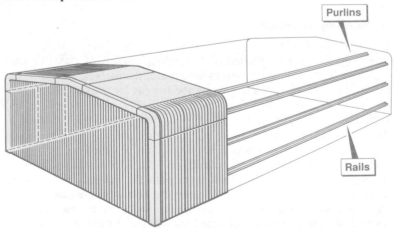

Fig. 5.16 Sketch illustrating typical framing and metal cladding.

This type of metal cladding is increasingly being used for finishing the roofs of commercial office buildings, leisure centres, schools etc. and is fixed to an appropriate metal or timber frame. The fixings vary widely and, in some cases, are extremely complicated to compensate for expansion, water penetration, building movement, wind etc.

The metals used eg. steel, aluminium, copper, lead, zinc are alloys depending on what type of "finish" is required. The metal can be shaped over practically any former as illustrated in Plate 6.

(4) Decking

Decking is usually found in flat or nearly flat roofs. The supports can be steel or aluminium girders or tubing, timber or reinforced concrete. The decking can be made up of almost any type of board eg. fibreboard, strawboard and weatherproofed with layers of asphalt or bitumenised roofing felt, possibly heat sealed and topped off with a further protective layer of tiles or heat reflecting material. Generally these roofs are safe for firefighters to work on but that will depend on the size of the fire beneath them and the strength of the roof supports.

h. Behaviour of roofs and roofing material in fire

(1) General

Roof coverings are, in general, non-combustible or, at least, not readily combustible (an exception being thatch) so a roof is not normally vulnerable to fire from an external source. Generally it is the way roofs are built rather than the material used that causes difficulties for firefighters. The pitched roof presents problems because of the large unused spaces that exist ie. lofts, attics voids etc. between the ceiling of the rooms below and the weather covering. As stated elsewhere these voids can extend, unbroken, over several dwellings or, in some cases, over the whole of the building. The amount of timber present, often of light cross-sectional area, the rising heat and smoke from a fire in the building coupled with the fact that there is seldom easy access to these areas from below or through the roof covering, means spread of fire into the void presents a difficult and punishing period of firefighting.

(2) Fireblocking

Most modern residential buildings with this type of roof are "fireblocked" ie. where required in construction, fire-resisting foam blocks are inserted to prevent fire spreading through cavities up into the roof. The roofs are also compartmented and precautions are taken to stop fire spread from one void to another including over the top of the compartment division.

(3) Connectors

As mentioned in Chapter 11 Section 2, a modern trend is for the light timber in roofs to be put together with metal connectors. These have been known to expand and fall out in a fire and leave the roof unsupported with the certainty of roof collapse.

(4) Slates and tiles

A fire attacking the underside of a pitched roof can release slates or tiles and these can slide off causing injuries to firefighters below. The rate at which this can happen will be dictated by whether the roof is underdrawn with closeboarding or only with felt.

(5) Steelwork

Steelwork or wrought-iron, especially of light section, is vulnerable to a fierce fire and a fairly rapid collapse can follow when the steelwork is unprotected. A lot will depend on the type of roof it is supporting and whether there is any roof venting eg. automatic vents, thermoplastic rooflights.

(6) Cast-iron

Cast-iron is of greater cross-section and density then steel and such trusses can still be found in place after a fire providing there has not been a sharp change in temperature ie a heated truss struck by a jet.

(7) Trussing and cladding

The complicated trussing in, for instance, a cinema or theatre roof is usually light section. Although protected by the auditorium ceiling firefighters must be aware of the possibility of a complete collapse in a large fire. The reaction of the newer insulated metal-clad roofs will depend largely on the types of support and the fixings. Both will be of light construction and, again, venting of the roof will keep the temperature down and the roof up.

(8) Concrete

Concrete is usually reinforced in some way and providing the steelwork is not exposed quickly to the fire eg. by spalling of the concrete cover, it will maintain its support.

Part 3
Building design

Where fire is concerned the most important contents of a building are its occupants and it is their protection which should be uppermost in the mind of the architect. In all buildings or structures the time taken for the occupants to reach a place of safety is important. To do this it is necessary to ensure that, if a fire breaks out in one section, its effect on other sections is minimal for as long as possible to enable people to get out safely. This can be accomplished in several ways and this Part attempts to explain how.

However, the trend towards very high large buildings providing accommodation for several thousand people could mean evacuation times beyond the normal requirements. Thought has had to be given to allowing people to move away from the fire area eg. up two floors, to a place of "relative safety" without actually leaving the building. Obviously such a building has to be carefully designed and maintained.

Where buildings cannot be physically separated into "safe" zones eg. large warehouses, the effects of fire can be mitigated either by restricting the number of people who work there or by built-in fire protection (see the Manual Book 9).

Fire can spread from outside of the building and the Building Regulations recognise this and legislate accordingly. Once a fire does start the brigade will need to tackle it and to do that firefighters need good access for themselves and their appliances and equipment. Building Regulations have up-dated the old document 1/70 and now lay down the requirements for access.

Chapter 6
Compartmentation

1 Introduction

To prevent the spread of fire within buildings provision is made to sub-divide the building into compartments with restricted floor or cubic capacity. This is done by means of compartment walls and compartment floors which are elements of structure and therefore require fire resistance. The object is two-fold:

(a) to prevent rapid fire spread which could trap occupants of the building and

(b) to reduce the chance of fires becoming large, on the basis that large fires are more dangerous not only to occupants but to people in the vicinity of the building.

2 Degree of sub-division.

This depends on :

(a) the use of the building, which affects the potential for fires and the severity of fires, as well as the ease of evacuation;

(b) the height of the top storey of the building which is an indication of the ease of evacuation and the ability of the fire service to intervene effectively; and

(c) the availability of a sprinkler system which affects the growth rate of the fire and may suppress it altogether.

Generally, in single storey buildings, the life risk associated with a fire involving a whole building is less than with a multi-storey building. The provisions for compartmentation of single-storey buildings only apply, therefore, to those having a significant sleeping risk. There are, however, requirements for compartmentation of most multi-storey buildings. The maximum dimensions for buildings or compartments are given in Table 4.

3 Requirements

Every compartment wall and compartment floor should

(a) form a complete barrier to fire between the compartments they separate;

(b) have the appropriate fire resistance according to their user group and

(c) where needed (together with any beam or column which forms part of the wall, and any structure which carries it) be constructed of materials of limited combustibility.

(d) a compartment wall which is used to form a separate part of a building should run the full height of the building in the same continuous vertical plane. It should be taken up above the roof or the roof should resist fire penetration and spread (see Fig. 6.1).

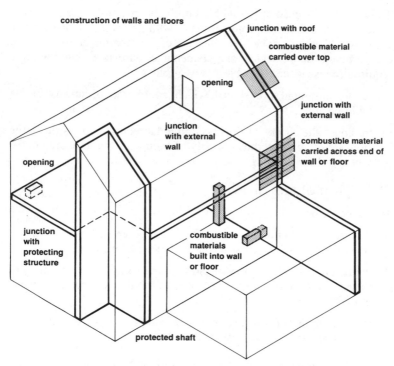

Fig. 6.1 Diagram illustrating various aspects of compartmentation.

(e) where a compartment wall or floor meets another compartment wall, or an external wall, separating wall or protected shaft, they should be bonded together or firestopped.

(f) spaces that connect compartments, such as stairways and service shafts, need to be protected to restrict fire spread between the compartments, and they are termed protected shafts (see Fig. 6.2)

4 Requirements for different building groups.

a. All purpose

   (i) a wall common to two or more buildings (separating walls) should be constructed as a compartment wall.

protected shafts provide for the movement of people (eg stairs, lifts), or things (eg services pipes), or air (eg ventilation shaft) between different compartments. The structure enclosing the shaft (unless formed by adjacent external, compartment, or separating walls) is called **protecting structure.** The diagram shows three common examples which illustrate the principles.

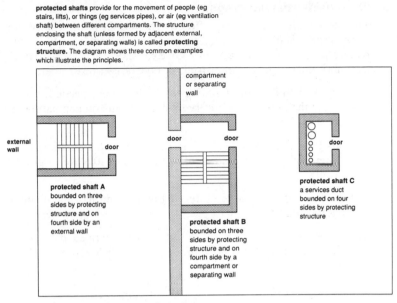

Fig. 6.2 Examples of protected shafts.

(ii) compartment walls and/or floors should be provided to separate parts of a building that are occupied mainly for different purposes, from one another. This does not apply where one of the different purposes is ancillary to the other.

b. Flats and maisonettes

In buildings containing flats or maisonettes the following should be constructed as compartment walls or compartment floors;

(i) any floor (unless it is within a maisonette ie. between one storey and another within a dwelling) and

(ii) any wall separating a flat or maisonette from any other part of the building and

(iii) any wall enclosing a refuse chamber.

c. Institutional buildings.

(i) in institutional purpose group buildings all floors should be constructed as compartment floors.

(ii) any walls needed to divide the storeys of a hospital into two compartments to comply with means of escape provisions should be constructed as compartment walls.

d. Other residential buildings.

Any floors in buildings of the other residential purpose group should be constructed as compartment floors.

e. Non-residential buildings.

The following walls and floors should be constructed as compartment walls and compartment floors in buildings of a non-residential purpose group ie. Office, shop and commercial, assembly and recreation, industrial, storage or non-residential.

(i) any wall (unless the building is single storey) needed to subdivide the building to observe the size limits on compartments given in Table 4;

(ii) any floor if the building, or separated part of the building, has a storey with a floor at a height of more than 30m above ground level;

(iii) the floor of the ground storey if the building has one or more basements;

(iv) any basement floor if the building, or separated part, has a basement at a depth of more than 10m below ground floor level.

5 Junctions of compartment walls and roof.

(a) A compartment wall should be taken up to meet the underside of the roof covering or deck with firestopping where necessary at the wall/roof junction to maintain the continuity of fire resistance. The use of a cavity barrier instead of continuing the compartment wall past the ceiling level is not allowed, as the performance standard of the barrier is lower than that of the compartment wall.

(b) If a fire penetrates the roof near a compartment wall there is a risk that it will spread over the roof to an adjoining compartment. A 1.5m strip either side of the wall, where it meets the roof, constructed of a designated type of covering on a non-combustible substrate or deck, is required to reduce this risk.

(c) In buildings not more than 15m high in certain purpose groups, other types of substrate to the roof covering may carried over the compartment wall providing they are fully bedded in mortar over the width of the wall (see Fig. 6.3).

6 Permitted openings.

There must, obviously, be some communication between compartments and the Regulations restrict these and set standards of protection required in the various appendices to the Approved Document.

a. Openings in separating walls

Any openings in a wall which is common to two or more buildings should be limited to those for;

(i) a door which is needed to provide a means of escape in case of

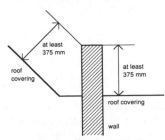

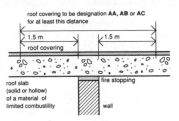

(a) Building or compartment at any height and use

(b) Building or compartment at any height and use

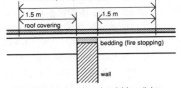

boarding (used as a substrate), wood wool slabs, or timber tiling battens may be carried over the wall provided that they are fully bodded in mortar (or other not less suitable material) where over the wall

(c) Building or compartment residential (except institution) office or assembly use and not more than 15m above mean ground level

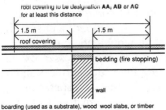

boarding (used as a substrate), wood wool slabs, or timber tiling battens may be carried over the wall provided that they are fully bedded in mortar (or other not less suitable material) where over the wall

(d) Dwelling house up to 3 storeys

Fig. 6.3 Junctions of compartment walls and roof.

fire and which has the same fire resistance as that required for the wall and is fitted in accordance with the relevant provisions;

(ii) the passage of a pipe which meets the relevant provisions.

b. Openings in other compartment walls or compartment floors.

Openings in compartment walls (other than those described in (a) above) or compartment floors should be limited to those for:-

(i) doors which have the appropriate fire resistance given in Table 3 and are fitted in accordance with the relevant provisions;

(ii) the passage of pipes, ventilation ducts, chimneys, appliance ventilation ducts or ducts encasing one or more flue pipes which meet the relevant provisions;

(iii) refuse chutes of non-combustible construction;

(iv) protected shafts which meet the relevant provisions.

7 Other requirements.

The AD goes on to lay down the requirements for:

(a) protected shafts

(b) concealed spaces (cavities)

(c) fire-stopping

(d) car-parks

8 Shopping complexes.

Whilst the provisions in the AD regarding shops should generally be capable of application in cases where a shop is contained in a single separate building, complications may arise where a shop forms part of a complex or comprehensive development.

These may include covered malls providing access to a number of shops and common servicing areas. In particular the provisions about maximum compartment size may be difficult to meet bearing in mind that it would not be practical to compartment a shop from a mall serving it. To a lesser extent the provisions about fire resistance, separating walls, surfaces and boundary distances may pose problems.

To ensure a satisfactory standard of fire safety in shopping complexes alternative and compensatory features to those already set out in the AD are included. These are

(a) unified management of the complex;

(b) adequate means of escape and smoke control provisions;

(c) sprinkler protection of all shop units, storage and service areas and any parts of the malls used for a purpose that might introduce a fire load into the mall;

(d) a fire alarm system incorporating automatic fire detection in non-public areas;

(e) access for firefighting purposes;

(f) Construction consisting generally of materials of limited combustibility except for limited decorative features and limited amounts of materials in shop facias having a lesser standard of surface spread of flame characteristics than those for the walls in circulation areas;

(g) walls and floors between shop units constructed as compartment walls and compartment floors;

(h) floors in any shop in it exceeding 2000m^2 in area constructed as compartment floors;

(i) floors in any shop unit opening onto the mall at more than one level constructed as compartment floors.

(j) compartmentation also provided between a large shop unit (over 3700m^2 in area) and a mall, or between opposing large shop units (each over 2000m^2) and a mall. This compartmentation could be provided by fire shutters (smaller shop units would normally not be compartmented from a mall).

Plate 1. An example of sprayed-on fire protection.
Photo: Essex Fire Brigade.

Plate 2. Use of castellated beams in a light roof construction.
Photo: Essex Fire Brigade.

Plate 3. Steel reinforcement ready to be encased in concrete.
Photo: Trent Concrete

Plate 4. Type of concrete "plank" showing its final position right.
Photo: Essex Fire Brigade.

Plate 5. Typical light steelwork and fibreboard partition.
Photo: Essex Fire Brigade.

Plate 6. An example of metal cladding designed to be a particular feature of a roof.
Photo: Broderick Structures.

Plate 7. Steelwork of various sizes in a framed building. Part concrete "plank" and part poured concrete floor. Note concrete cladding on lower column.
Photo: Essex Fire Brigade.

Plate 8. A large roof basically supported by cantilever from a steel framed tower.
Photo: Nicholas Grimshaw and Partners Ltd.

Plate 9. A supermarket showing the method of suspended roof support.
Photo: Ernest Ireland Construction.

Plate 10. Early stage in a lift-slab construction (see Plates 11 and 12).
Photo: Douglas Specialist Contractors Ltd.

Plate 11. Lift-slab construction in its middle stages (see Plates 10 and 12).
Photo: Douglas Specialist Contractors Ltd.

Plate 12. Lift-slab construction with all floors in position and shell well advanced (see Plates 10 and 11).
Photo: Douglas Specialist Contractors Ltd.

Plate 13. Interior of an ultra-modern hotel. The central lift shaft can be seen left. Note the fire detector left of the sculpture and unopenable windows to the atrium
Photo: Heathrow Sterling Hotel

Plate 14. A nucleus designed hospital built onto an older complex top left.
Photo: Ahrends, Burton and Koralek.

Plate 15. Leisure centre constructed of glulam showing some of the spans
and curves achievable in this type of material.
Photo: Technical Timber Services.

Plate 16. Modern office construction with atrium. Fire detectors are visible at second floor level.
Photo: The Fitzroy Robinson Partnership.

Plate 17. Interior of offices under construction (see Plate 18).
Photo: Richard Turpin.

Plate 18. Exterior of Plate 17 showing almost total glazing with services at each end.
Photo: Richard Turpin.

Plate 19. Typical atrium of an office block. All the vertical glass is of the "Pyrostop" fire-resistant type.
Photo: Pilkington Glass

Plate 20. A high-bay warehouse 155m x 55m x 22m, totally enclosed. The six large smoke outlets are repeated at the other end (see Plate 21).
Photo: Rowntrees Mackintosh.

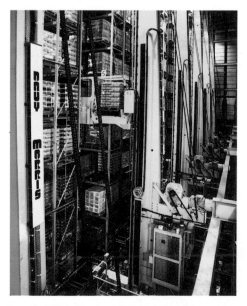

Plate 21. The interior of a high-bay warehouse showing automatic picking cranes and the extremely restricted conditions in the racking area.
Photo: Rowntrees Mackintosh.

Plate 22. Concrete being poured onto a combination of steelwork and polystyrene formers to construct a "honeycomb" roof.
Photo: Essex Fire Brigade.

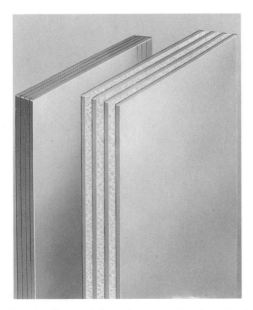

Plate 23. Pyrostop fire-resisting glass showing how the intumescent layers react to heat.
Photo: Pilkington Glass.

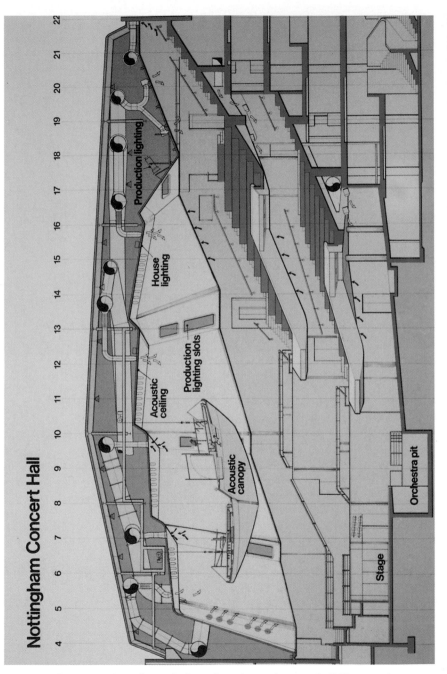

Plate 24. Side elevation of a typical modern theatre/concert hall illustrated
in Plate 24.
Photo: RHWL Partnership.

Plate 25. Interior of the theatre/concert hall illustrated in Plate 24.
Photo: RHWL Partnership.

Plate 26. Pyrostop fire-resisting glass providing fire separation to a staircase in a public library.
Photo: Pilkington Glass.

Plate 27. A suspended fabric roof to modern laboratories.
Photo: Michael Hopkins and Partners.

Plate 28. Large fixed glazing upstand over a shopping mall. The surface in the foreground is a rubberised flexible membrane providing weatherproofing for the roof.
Photo: Essex Fire Brigade.

Plate 29. Polystyrene insulating sheeting placed between the inner wall and the brick cladding.
Photo: Essex Fire Brigade.

Plate 30. A specially designed cladding system fitted to an inner hollow-brick wall.
Photo: Langley London Ltd.

Plate 31. An example where the strawboard roof lining assisted the spread of the fire.
Photo: Tyne and Wear Fire Brigade.

Plate 32. Blockwork wall severely distorted but still intact following a fire.
Photo: Cheshire Fire Brigade.

Guidance on proposals for shopping complexes is given in BS5588 Part 10 and on smoke control in a BRE report called "Design principles for smoke ventilation in enclosed shopping centres". Table 4 gives the maximum dimensions of a building or compartment in multi-storied buildings.

Table 4 Maximum dimensions of building or compartment (multi-storey non-residential buildings)

Purpose group of building (or part)	Height of floor of top storey above ground level (m)	Floor area of any one storey in the building or compartment (m²)
Office	no limit	no limit
Assembly & Recreation Shop & Commercial:		
not sprinklered	no limit	2000
sprinklered (1)	no limit	4000
Industrial (3):		
not sprinklered	not more than 20	7000
	more than 20	2000 (2)
sprinklered (1)	not more than 20	14000
	more than 20	4000 (2)

	Height of floor oft top storey above ground level (m)	Maximum compartment volume (m³)
Storage (3) & Other non-residential: a. car park for light vehicles	no limit	no limit
b. any other building or part: -not sprinklered	not more than 20	20000
	more than 20	4000 (2)
-sprinklered (1)	not more than 20	40000
	more than 20	8000 (2)

Notes:
1. "Sprinklered" means that the building is fitted throughout with an automatic sprinkler system meeting the relevant recommendations of BS5306: Part 2, ie the relevant occupancy rating together with the additional requirements for life safety.
2. This reduced area limit applies only to storeys that are more than 20m above ground level.
3. There may be additional limitations on floor area and/or sprinkler provisions in certain industrial and storage uses under other legislation, for example in respect of storage of LPG and certain chemicals.

Chapter 7
Fire Spread

1 Internal fire spread (linings)

a. General

The requirements of AD B2, regarding internal linings, will be met if the spread of fire over the internal linings of the building is restricted by making provision for them to

(i) have low rates of flame surface spread of flame and

(ii) have, if ignited, a rate of heat release which is reasonable in the circumstances,

in order to limit the contribution that the fabric of the building makes to fire growth.

The choice of materials for the linings of walls and ceilings can significantly affect the spread of fire and its rate of growth even though they are not likely to be the materials first ignited. This is particularly so in circulation spaces where linings would offer the main vehicle of fire spread and where rapid spread could prevent occupants from escaping.

b. Floors and stairs.

The requirements of AD B2 do not apply to the upper surfaces of floors and stairs because they are not significantly involved in a fire until it is well developed and do not play an important part in fire spread in the early stages that are most relevant to the safety of the occupants.

c. Furniture and fittings.

Furniture and fittings can have a major effect on fire spread but Building Regulations are not the place to attempt to control them. They are controlled by legislation explained in Chapter 10.

d. Classification of performance of materials.

The different classes of performance and appropriate methods of testing are described in Appendix A of the AD. The main classifications used are based on tests in the BS 476; Parts 6 and 7 but for classifications of thermoplastic materials tests are under BS 2782 and BS 5438.

2 Definitions, internal

Ceiling –   a part of a building which encloses and is exposed overhead in a room or circulation space.

Circulation space – a space (including a protected stairway) mainly used as a means of access between a room and an exit from the building or compartment.

Rooflight – any domelight, lantern light, skylight or other element intended to admit daylight through the roof.

Room – an enclosed space in a building that is not an enclosed circulation space. (Thus the term includes not only conventional rooms but also cupboards that are not fittings and large spaces such as warehouses and auditoria).

Thermoplastic material - this has a specific definition laid out in Appendix A to the AD as follows:

Any polymeric material which has a softening point below 200°C if tested to BS 2782; Part 1; Method 120a; 1976. For the purposes of ADB2 thermoplastic materials are classified TP(a), (b) or (c) and Appendix A describes the differences.

3 General provisions.

The surface linings of walls and ceilings should meet the following classifications:

Class 3 in bathrooms and toilets

Class 1 in other rooms

Class 1 in circulation spaces within dwellings

Class 0 in other circulation spaces (including the common areas of flats and maisonettes)

NB. Class 0 is a higher classification than Class 1. It is not identified in any BS. but a definition is given in Appendix A of the AD. To be included in BS 476 Pt. 14

The ADB2 continues in specifying special provisions for walls, fire-resisting ceilings, fire-protecting suspended ceilings, thermoplastic materials, windows and rooflights. Limits are also set on the type and construction of lighting diffusers in certain areas.

4 External fire spread

General

In the Building Regulations, AD B4 describes the requirements necessary to ensure adequate space separation between buildings to prevent external fire spread. These will be met if:

(a) the external walls are constructed so that the risk of ignition from an external source, and the spread of fire over the surfaces, is restricted by making provision for them to have low rates of spread of flame and, in some cases, low rates of heat release;

(b) the amount of unprotected area in the side of a building is restricted so as to limit the amount of thermal radiation that can pass through the wall, taking the distance between the wall and the boundary into account;

(c) the roof is constructed so that the risk of spread of fire and/or fire penetration from an external fire source is restricted;

in each case so as to limit the risk of a fire spreading from the building to a building beyond the boundary or vice-versa. The extent to which this is necessary is dependent on the use of the building and its distance from the boundary and, in some cases, its height.

5 Definitions, external

(a) Boundary
The boundary of the land belonging to the building or, where the land abuts a road, railway, canal or river, the centreline of that road, railway, canal or river (Fig. 7.1).

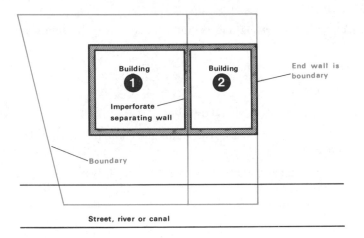

Fig. 7.1 Examples of the term "boundary".

(b) External wall (or side of building)
Includes a part of a roof pitched at an angle of 70% or more to the horizontal – if that part of the roof adjoins a space within a building to which persons have access.

(c) Notional boundary
A boundary presumed to exist between buildings on the same site (Fig. 7.2). This concept is only applied to buildings in the residential, assembly and recreational purpose groups.

(d) Relevant boundary
   The boundary which the side of the building faces (see Fig. 7.1). A
   notional boundary can be a relevant boundary

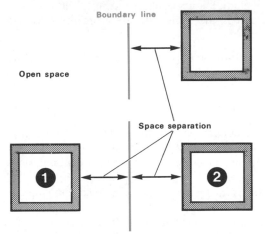

Boundary line

Open space

Space separation

1 2

Fig. 7.2 The total space between two similar buildings is calculated by taking the distance from each building to its boundary.

(e) Unprotected area In relation to a side or external wall of a building this means:

(i)   a window or other opening;

(ii) any part of an external wall which has less than the relevant fire resistance set out in the provisions;

(iii) any part of the external wall which has combustible material more than 1mm thick attached or applied to its external face whether for cladding or any other purpose.
      (combustible material, in this context, is that *not* included in Tables set out in appendix A to the AD).

6 Space separation

The whole concept of the space separation provisions is to limit the extent of openings and areas which will not give adequate protection against the spread of fire. These provisions assume:

(a) that the size of the fire will depend on the compartmentation of the building so that the fire will involve a complete compartment but will not spread across lines of compartmentation;

(b) that the intensity of a fire is related to the use of the building (ie. purpose group) but that it can be moderated by a sprinkler system;

(c) that residential, assembly and recreational purpose groups represent a greater life risk than other uses;

(d) that apart from uses in (c) above, the spread of fire between buildings on the same site represents a low life risk;

(e) that the building on the adjoining site has an identical elevation to the one in question and is the same distance from the common boundary;

(f) that no significant radiation will pass through any parts of the external wall that have fire resistance.

7 Boundaries

The use of the distance to a boundary rather that to another building, in measuring the separation distance, makes it possible to calculate the allowable proportion of unprotected areas even where a building does not exist but may in the future.

A wall should be treated as facing a boundary if it makes an angle of 80 degrees with it or less (see Fig. 7.1).

The boundary which a wall faces, whether it is a boundary of the site or a notional boundary, is called the *relevant boundary*.

8 External walls

(a) A wall situated within 1m from any point on the relevant boundary will meet the provisions for space separation if:

   (i)   the only unprotected areas are those shown in Fig. 7.3;

   (ii) the rest of the wall is fire-resisting.

(b) A wall situated at least 1m from any point on the relevant boundary will meet the provisions of space separation if:

   (i)   the extent of unprotected areas does not exceed that given by one of the methods referred to in the Fire Research Technical Paper No. 5, 1963 and the BRE report "Building separation and boundary distances (see 9 below);

   (ii) the rest of the wall is fire-resisting.

9 Basis for calculating acceptable unprotected area

Section 8(b)(i) above mentions the methods of calculation to determine acceptable unprotected areas.

The aim is to ensure that the building is separated from the boundary by at least half the distance at which the thermal radiation intensity emitted from all unprotected areas in the wall would be $12.6kW/m^2$ assuming the radiation intensity at each unprotected area is:-

(a) $84kW/m^2$ if the building is in the residential, office, assembly and recreation purpose groups;

Unprotected areas which may be disregarded in assessing the separation distance from the boundary

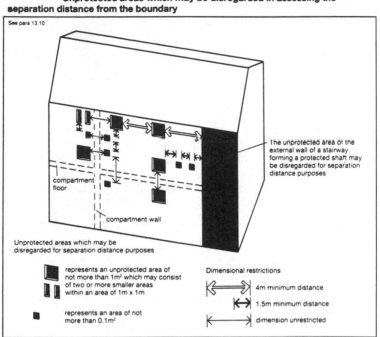

Fig. 7.3 Extract from ADB4.

(b) 168kW/m² if the building is in the shop, commercial industrial, storage or other non-residential purpose groups.

(c) It may be assumed that the intensity of radiation from a fire in a compartment which is fitted throughout with a sprinkler system will be half the values given in (a) and (b) above. The system should meet the relevant recommendations of BS 5306 Part 2.

10 Canopies

An interesting exception to the above provisions is with canopies which do not fall within Class VI of Schedule 3 of the Building Regulations and do not meet the criteria for size and boundary distance.

Chapter 8
Access to Buildings

1 General

When fire occurs in a building it is essential that fire appliances and personnel can approach the building as quickly as possible. The PDA will depend not only on the use or purpose group of the building but also on its height and size.

Different types of appliances will require different access conditions eg. the turning circle of a turntable ladder will be larger than that of a pumping appliance and probably the clearance height will also be greater.

The Building Regulations now include measures to assist the Fire Service in gaining access to buildings. In Section B5 of the AD the requirements will be met if the building:

(a) has sufficient means of external access to enable fire appliances to be brought near to it for effective use;

(b) has sufficient means of access into it and within it to enable firefighting personnel to enter for the purpose of fighting fire and effecting rescue;

(c) is provided with sufficient internal fire mains and other facilities to assist firefighters in their tasks;

(d) if the building is provided with adequate means of venting heat and smoke from a fire in a basement;

all to an extent dependent on the use and size of the building and the safety of people in and around the building.

2 Definitions.

Firefighting lift.
A lift designed to have additional protection with controls that enable it to be used under the direct control of the fire brigade in fighting a fire.

Firefighting lobby.
A protected lobby for providing access from a firefighting stairway to the accommodation area and to any associated firefighting lift.

Firefighting shaft.
A protected shaft containing a firefighting stairway, firefighting lobbies and, if provided, a firefighting lift.

Firefighting stairway.

A protected stairway communicating with the accommodation area only through a firefighting lobby.

Perimeter.

The perimeter excludes separating walls. An example of a building "footprint" and perimeter is shown in Fig. 8.1.

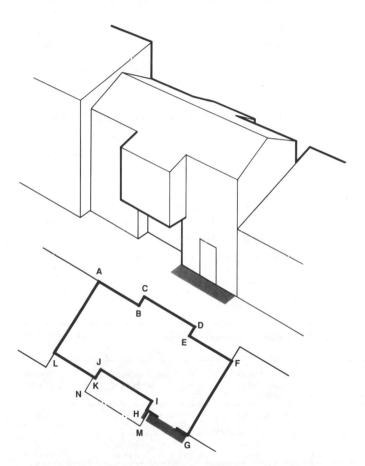

Plan of building AFGL where AL and FG are walls in common with other buildings.

The footprint of the building is the maximum aggregate plan perimeter found by the vertical projection of any overhanging storey onto a ground storey. (i.e. ABCDEFGHMNKL)

The perimeter of the building for the purposes of Table 5 is the sum of the lengths of the two external walls, taking account of the footprint, i.e. (A to B to C to D to E to F) + (G to H to M to N to K to L).

If the dimensions of the building were such that Table 5 requires vehicle access the tone illustrates one possible example of 15% of the perimeter. Note that there should be a door into the building in this length.

If the building does not have walls in common with other buildings, the lengths AL and FG would be included in the perimeter.

Fig. 8.1 Example of a building "footprint" and perimeter.

3 Fire mains.

a. General

Fire mains are pipes installed in a building and equipped so that the Fire Service may connect hose to receive a supply of water for firefighting inside the building. A description of these systems will be found in the Manual, Book 9, Chapter 8.

b. Provision of fire mains.

Fire mains in buildings should be provided to the following standards:

(i) Storeys above ground level, in buildings with a floor at more than 20m above ground level, should be equipped with dry rising fire mains.

(ii) Basements in buildings with a basement at more than 10m below ground level should be equipped with dry fire mains.

(iii) Storeys above ground level, in buildings with a floor at more than 60m above ground level, should be equipped with wet rising fire mains.

(iv) Where fire mains are installed they should be positioned so that, at each level other than ground level, there is one main for every firefighting shaft provided.

(v) The outlets from fire mains should be sited in:

(a) a firefighting shaft;

(b) a protected stairway or

Table 5 Fire service vehicle access to buildings not fitted with fire mains

Total floor[1] area of building m²	Height of floor of top storey above ground m	Provide vehicle access to:	Type of appliance
up to 2000	up to 9	see paragraph 16.2	pump
	over 9	15% of perimeter	high reach
2000-8000	up to 9	15% of perimeter	pump
	over 9	50% of perimeter	high reach
8000-16,000	up to 9	50% of perimeter	pump
	over 9	50% of perimeter	high reach
16,000-24,000	up to 9	75% of perimeter	pump
	over 9	75% of perimeter	high reach
over 24,000	up to 9	100% of perimeter	pump
	over 9	100% of perimeter	high reach

N.B. The total floor area is the aggregate of all the floors in the building.

16.2 There should be vehicle access to small buildings (those of up to 2000m² with a top storey less than 9m above ground level) to within 45m of any point on the projected plan area (or 'footprint' (see Fig 8.1) of the building.

  (c) a balcony or walkway in the open air.

 (vi) The design and construction of fire mains should be in accordance with the relevant sections of BS 5306 Part 1 1976.

4 Vehicle access.

The general vehicle access requirements are shown in Table 5 for buildings without fire mains. These do not apply to buildings with fire mains.

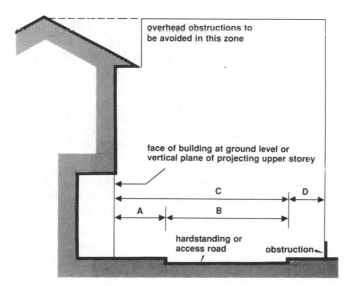

	Type of appliance Turntable ladder Dimension (m)	Hydraulic platform Dimension (m)
A. Maximum distance at near edge of hardstanding from building	4.9	2.0
B. Minimum width of hardstanding	5.0	5.5
C. Minimum distance of further edge of hardstanding from building	10.0	7.5
D. Minimum width of unobstructed space (for swing of appliance platform)	N.A.	2.2

Note:
Hardstanding for high reach appliances should be as level as possible and should not exceed a gradient of 1 in 12.

Fig. 8.2 Relationship between building and hardstanding/access roads for high-reach fire appliances

a. Dry mains

In buildings fitted with fire mains appliances only need access to the perimeter at points near the mains, where firefighters can enter the building and where, in the case of dry mains, a hose connection can be made from the appliance to pump water into the main. Access for the pumping appliance should be to within 18m of each fire main inlet, and the inlet should be visible from the appliance.

b. Wet mains.

In the case of a building fitted with wet mains the access should be to within 18m, and within sight of, a suitable entrance giving access to the main and within sight of the inlet for the emergency replenishment of the suction tank serving the main.

c. Vehicle routes and hardstandings

   (i)   A vehicle access route may be a public or private road, or other route, which, including any manhole or other covers, meets the standards of Table 6.

  (ii)   Access routes to buildings with any storey at more than 10m above ground level should meet the standards of "high reach" appliances eg. aerials. For lower buildings the access should be to the standards for pumping appliances (see Fig. 8.2).

 (iii)   Where access is provided to an elevation in accordance with Table 6, overhead obstructions eg. cables and branches, that would interfere with the pitching of ladders etc. should be avoided in that area.

Table 6 Vehicle access route specifications.

Appliance type	Minimum width of road between kerbs (m)	Minimum width of gateways (m)	Mimimum turning circle between kerbs (m)	Minimum turning circle between walls (m)	Minimum clearance height (m)	Minimum carrying capacity (tonnes)
Pump	3.7	3.1	16.8	19.2	3.7	12.5
High Reach	3.7	3.1	29	29	4	17.00

N.B. Fire appliances are not standardised. The figures above will cater for most appliances in use in 1990 but, obviously, Fire Authorities can, and will, use appliances which could need different specifications.

5 Access to buildings for firefighters.

a. General

In low rise buildings, without deep basements, requirements for firefighters' access will be met by a combination of the normal means of escape and the measures for appliance access which give ladder access to upper storeys. In other buildings the problems of reaching the fire and firefighting merit the provision of additional facilities so that firefighters can take quick, effective action from a secure operating base.

These additional facilities include

firefighting lifts
firefighting stairways
firefighting lobbies

which combine in a protected shaft known as a firefighting shaft.

b. Provision of firefighting shafts.

(i)   Buildings with a floor more than 20m above ground level or with a basement at more than 10m below ground level, should be provided with firefighting shafts.

(ii) Every firefighting stairway and firefighting lift should be approached through a firefighting lobby.

(iii) A firefighting stairway should serve every storey of the building. However, in large buildings where the floor area at upper levels is significantly less than at lower levels (eg. podium or tower) it may be acceptable to terminate a firefighting shaft at an intermediate storey. This can be done provided that the criteria for the number and location of firefighting shafts are satisfied and that there is a clear indication at the ground level entrance to the shaft that it does not serve every storey.

c. Firefighting lifts.

A firefighting lift does not necessarily have to serve every storey.

(i)   a firefighting lift should serve every storey above ground, including the ground floor, in a building with a floor above 20m above ground;

(ii) a firefighting lift should serve every storey below ground, and the ground floor, in a building with a basement at more than 10m below ground;

(iii) however, a firefighting lift need not serve a storey in a building used as flats in which there is no entrance to a dwelling, and it need not serve the top storey of a building.

d. Number and location of firefighting shafts.

The number of firefighting shafts should:

(i)   (if the building is fitted throughout with an automatic sprinkler system meeting BS 5306 Part 2) comply with Table 3; or

(ii) (if a building is not fitted with sprinklers) be such that there is at least one for every 900m² (or part thereof) of floor area of the largest floor that is more than 20m above ground level.

The location of firefighting shafts should be such that every part of every storey, other than fire service access level, is no more than 60m from the entrance to a firefighting lobby measured on a route suitable for laying hose. In the event that the internal layout is unknown at the design stage then every part of every such storey should be no more than 40m in a direct line from the entrance of a firefighting lobby.

Table 7 Minimum number of firefighting shafts in buildings fitted with sprinklers.

Floor area of largest storey over 20m above ground level. (m²)	Minimum number of firefighting shafts.
less than 900	1
900 to 2000	2
over 2000	2 plus 1 for every 1500m² of floor area or part thereof.

e. Design and construction of firefighting shafts.

All firefighting shafts should be equipped with fire mains having outlet connections and valves in every firefighting lobby except at access level. Firefighting shafts should be designed and installed in accordance with BS 5588 Part 5 1990 in respect of the following:

(i)   planning within the firefighting shaft

(ii) fire mains and landing valves

(iii) smoke control

(iv) fire resistance

(v)   firefighting lift installation

(vi) electrical supply

(vii) construction

Firefighting shaft walls should be of robust construction so that their fire resistance is unlikely to be impaired by mechanical damage.

6 Venting of heat and smoke from basements.

a. Introduction

In addition to any measures that may be needed to keep smoke from prejudicing the use of any firefighting shaft, there can be the need to remove smoke and heat from basements. Any products of combustion from basement fires tend to vent via stairways down which firefighters have to penetrate to tackle the fire. Venting the products of combustion by other means must improve visibility and reduce temperatures making search, rescue and firefighting less onerous.

b. Provision of smoke outlets.

Where practicable each basement space should have one, or more, smoke outlets. It is acceptable, however, where basements are deep and the perimeter outlets restricted, to vent spaces at their perimeters and allow internal spaces to be vented indirectly by firefighters opening internal doors. Compartmentation of a basement requires each compartment to have direct access to vent openings. The exceptions to basement venting requirements are:

(i)   a basement in a single family dwelling,

(ii)   a floor area of not more than 200m^2 and

(iii)   a floor not more than 3m below the adjacent ground level.

The combined clear cross-sectional area of all smoke outlets should not be less than 2.5% of the floor area of the storey they serve. Any outlet terminating in a readily accessible position should be covered by a panel, stallboard or pavement light. The area that is ventilated eg. sub-basement boiler room, should be indicated clearly.

Chapter 9
Building construction

1 General

It is necessary for firefighters to have some knowledge of the principal methods of building construction. In the Fire Service a system of classifying various types of building construction was used in compiling the old K433 fire report form.

The advent of the FDR1 discontinued this requirement but the 9 classifications are still a useful division of types despite the many variations built today. Table 8 gives these classifications.

Table 8 Types of building construction

No.	Building construction
1	Timber-framed walls without internal columns
2	Timber-framed walls with unprotected internal columns
3	Timber-framed walls with internal protected columns
4	Load-bearing walls without internal columns
5	Load-bearing walls with unprotected internal columns
6	Load-bearing walls with protected internal columns
7	Framed, unloaded walls without internal columns
8	Framed, unloaded walls with unprotected internal columns
9	Framed, unloaded walls with protected internal columns

It is interesting that types 1 and 2 are coming back into use. Type 1 now includes some very large glued laminated timber buildings with unsupported spans of 60m or more. Type 2 are reappearing as large houses with solid timber exposed columns harking back to medieval times.

Following a long period favouring concrete construction, steel framed buildings (type 9) are also being built in increasing numbers again.

These resurgences appear to stem from the availability of new materials, new methods of construction and new procedures in construction.

This chapter deals with some of the constructional methods used and will give examples of both traditional and new types of buildings.

2 Constructional methods

The possibility of collapse of a building at an incident has been an ever-present problem for firefighters and an ability to assess a situation is important. Any large fire or explosion can make a building potentially dangerous as what remains will be under a great deal more stress than usual. That is why Safety Officers are detailed at an incident for the specific purpose of detecting dangerous conditions and warning the officer-in-charge in time for him to make a decision on what action to take to safeguard personnel (see Chapter 3, section 7). Some of the traditional signs of stress are discussed in the Manual, Book 11, Chapter 4 but modern buildings include lightweight roofs, cladding (both heavy and light), curtain walling, large areas of glass or polycarbonates in relatively light framing, cantilevered support structures etc. Their behaviour has only been fire-tested usually as individual elements of structure: the reaction of the whole building, together with its internal fire loading, has not.

The new Building Regulations attempt to redress this situation by requiring the building to be stable and remain stable under fire conditions (see Chapter 3, section 3 (B3)).

a. Solid construction

Solid construction, often referred to as "traditional" or masonry construction, consists of load-bearing external walls which support the floors and roof. The materials most commonly used were brick, concrete blocks or stone. This form of construction was almost universal during, and before, the 19thC for all kinds of industrial and commercial buildings. The example shown in Fig. 9.1 is a warehouse but factories, cotton and woollen mills and old office blocks are all similarly built.

The walls are of solid brick or stone possibly one metre thick or more at the base but setting back on the upper floors. Cast-iron columns support either cast-iron or timber beams which are bedded into the load-bearing walls at either end. Where there are timber beams the commonest type of floor is made of 50 to 70mm solid wooden boards spanning from beam to beam. Many older buildings (in which cast-iron beams may have been used) have barrel vaults and a few of the later ones have concrete floors on filler joists. The commonest roof is slated and pitched on wooden rafters and purlins supported by roof trusses.

b. Structural steel frame construction

This type of building has a great advantage from a designers point of view in that, in its construction, the load of the floors and cladding is carried at each level by beams which, in turn, pass the load on to the columns.

Within a skeleton framework floor space, divided in a variety of ways, can be provided and a suitable non-load-bearing cladding material used as a weather and insulation wall. The skeleton of the building (Fig. 9.2) is made up of universal beams and columns designed to support the loads (static and rolling) on the floors, the cladding and the wind pressure. How the columns are arranged is

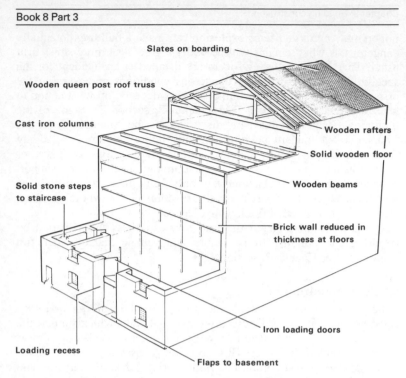

Slates on boarding

Wooden queen post roof truss

Cast iron columns

Wooden rafters

Solid wooden floor

Wooden beams

Solid stone steps to staircase

Brick wall reduced in thickness at floors

Iron loading doors

Loading recess

Flaps to basement

Fig. 9.1 Typical form of solid construction with loadbearing walls used during the 19th century for large buildings such as mills, warehouses, etc.

usually determined by the various circulation spaces in the building and, to some extent, the window openings (see Plate 7).

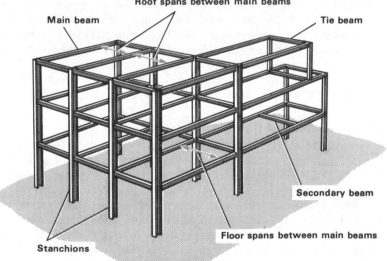

Roof spans between main beams

Main beam

Tie beam

Secondary beam

Floor spans between main beams

Stanchions

Fig. 9.2 An example of a structural steel frame for a building.

The steel work would, normally, be required to be protected against fire by either "solid" or "hollow" protection (see Chapter 4).

The technical advances in steel and its use in construction has enabled designers to be very innovative. It becomes difficult to equate a steel "frame" with some of the buildings already erected and in the process of erection. Huge frameworks are often assembled using tubular steel in a highly complicated manner and the remainder of the building is "hung" onto it. These examples may range from large multi-storey office blocks to some acres of one and two storey shopping and leisure centres.

An example is given in Plate 8 of a building virtually cantilevered out on cables from a tower at one end and, in Plate 9 is a similar, slightly more complicated, version.

These combinations of "traditional" steelwork, tubular steelwork and "light" steel, or other metal, frames, have not been tested in a large fire as yet (1991). Add to these frames large areas of glass or polycarbonates, metal-brick-concrete-plastic cladding, a variety of roofs including stretched fabric (see Plate 9), plus the internal fire loading and it becomes obvious that firefighters need to look at buildings with more than a passing interest.

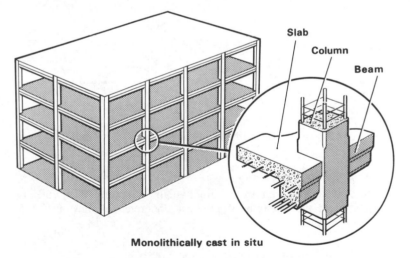

Fig. 9.3 In situ reinforced concrete frame construction.

c. Reinforced concrete construction.

The reinforced concrete frame was, when first used, treated as an alternative to steel frames ie. the columns supported the main beams which, in turn, supported the floor slabs. This, however, gradually changed to a monolithic type of construction (Fig. 9.3) where the columns, beams and floors were cast integrally. There has, recently, been a trend back to the original concept where the concrete floors are concrete slabs or planks laid between the beams (see Plate 4). Another variation is to lay metal shuttering between beams and then, leaving the shuttering in place, lay a concrete floor on top (see Fig. 4.10).

(1) Precast reinforced concrete frame

Here the reinforced concrete frame components are manufactured at the factory and then assembled on site in a similar manner to steel frames (see Fig. 9.4).

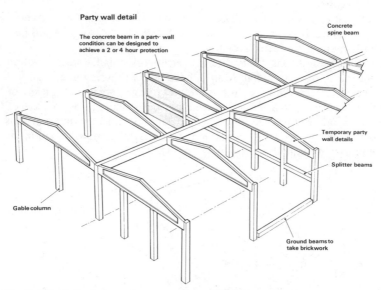

Party wall detail

The concrete beam in a party wall condition can be designed to achieve a 2 or 4 hour protection

Concrete spine beam

Temporary party wall details

Splitter beams

Gable column

Ground beams to take brickwork

Fig. 9.4 Typical reinforced concrete frame building.

(2) Composite construction

In this case the technology of lightweight structural steelwork is combined with the strength of pre-cast concrete columns. Fig. 9.5 shows an example.

3 Modular systems

The differences between modular systems, composite construction and pre-cast construction are blurred but the main advantage of most modular systems is that, within certain parameters, prefabricated components can be used in an almost unlimited variety of ways. This includes their positioning for varying floor heights, spans, vertical spacing etc. plus an ability to use the same cross-sectional component in different loading conditions. Most systems use specially designed connectors with which to assemble the building. These can be moulded into the precast columns or beams at whatever position suits the design of the building. An example of a connector system by Trent Concrete is

Typical frame component arrangement

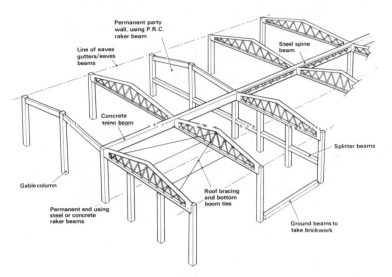

Fig. 9.5 Combination of lightweight steelwork and pre-cast concrete columns.

shown in Fig. 9.6. The steelwork in these components is usually encased in concrete and the steel connectors are covered in concrete in situ giving a degree of protection against fire and corrosion.

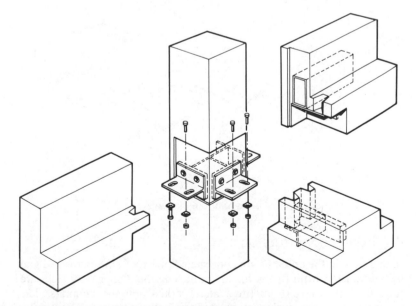

Fig. 9.6 Typical connector system for modular building.

Fig. 9.7 illustrates a multi-storey building, totally modular including floors, cladding, spandrels, stairs, columns and beams.

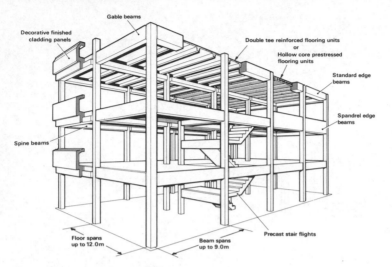

Fig. 9.7 A totally modular building.

Fig. 9.8 illustrates another type of modular building which includes modular roof sections.

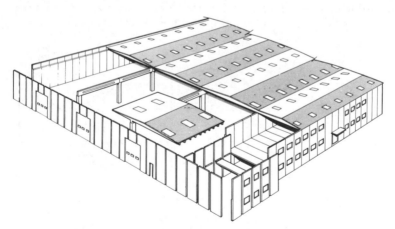

Fig. 9.8 Another example of a modular building system.

4 Liftslab construction

In this system the columns are constructed, the roof slab is formed and hydraulic jacks lift it first to the top of the column. Other floor slabs are formed and these too are lifted and "parked" on the columns. The sequence of lifting cycles is repeated until the structure is complete.

The columns are extended by "splicing" on another as the need arises. Plates 10 - 12 illustrate such a building in some of its stages of construction.

5 Portal frame construction

This type of construction has largely been superseded by composite or modular construction but is still utilised satisfactorily using either concrete, steel or glulam timber methods. The columns and roof members are continuous requiring little or no internal bracing and supporting the roof on a series of purlins (see Fig. 9.9). This gives a large unencumbered storage or working area.

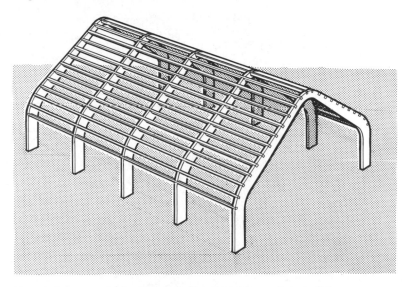

Fig. 9.9 Diagram of a laminated timber Portal frame for a building.

Part 4
Interior fire loading

In traditional furniture, fabrics and upholstery many natural materials are used whose burning characteristics are well-known eg. wood; cotton, wool and leather covers; upholstery filled with coir fibre and animal hair and feathers or kapok filled cushions. In contrast, modern counterparts can contain a bewildering variety of materials eg. flexible polyurethane, and other types of expanded foam covered with cottons, vinyls and acrylics and mixtures of cotton/polyester. The structure of the furniture could be rigid expanded polystyrene or polypropylene; curtains and carpets may be made of nylon or acrylic fibres and work surfaces of melamine formaldehyde or other plastics. In offices the traditional metal cabinets, drawers etc. are being replaced by polystyrene, polyurethane and polypropylene containers, trays and baskets.

Internal surfaces which used to be plaster or plasterboard now have polymeric decorative finishes eg. vinyl wall-paper, resin-impregnated-paper laminates (also used in door facings), polystyrene tiles, plastic mouldings and rigid polyurethane ceilings.

Tests carried out by the BRE have shown that many of these materials ignite easily, burn fiercely and give off copious amounts of thick, black, toxic smoke containing such gases as hydrochloric acid and hydrogen cyanide. The rapidity of smoke evolution impedes people trying to escape and they can be quickly overcome.

As a result of these tests and the mounting evidence linking the increase in deaths from smoke inhalation with the new materials, legislation has been introduced which controls their use and requires adequate measures to be taken to restrict ignition and flame spread.

A draft directive from the E.C. is being discussed in relation to the flammability of upholstered furniture intended for domestic use or use in public buildings. The following chapters explain some of the problems, refer to the tests carried out and comment on the legislation and Codes of Practice which are being, or have been, brought into use in the UK.

Chapter 10
Statistics, hazards and legislation

1 General

Building contents are a major factor, if not the major factor to be considered in relation to personal safety in fire. In the Post War Building Studies 'Fire Grading of Buildings' published in 1952, paragraph 48 states, " The danger to the occupants depends on the rate at which a fire spreads in the contents of the room and also on the linings of walls and ceilings'.

For the purposes of this section, the definitions of 'contents' is taken from the UK Fire Statistics published each year by the Home Office. In the published Tables, one particular section deals with 'Textiles, Upholstery and Furnishings' with applications covering clothing, beds and bedding, upholstered furniture, curtains and blinds, textile floorcoverings and other furnishings and furniture not listed.

The United Kingdom fire statistics published annually by the Home Office, show the significant contribution of textiles to the overall fire problem, particularly in domestic dwellings. The figures available in Tables 9 and 10 gives the following general picture :

Table 9

Fires in Dwellings	
Total Number of fires	64,200
Textiles, upholstery & furnishings	12,949
Clothing – on persons	152
Clothing – other	2,191
Other textiles	2,678
Bedding	4,850
Upholstery, covers	4,793
Curtains & blinds	795
Floor coverings	1,122
Other furnishings & furniture	305

Whilst it can be seen from Table 9 that, of the total number of fires in dwellings generally, about 20% are attributed to textiles, reference to Table 10 below shows that this percentage of fires accounts for around 67% of the total number of fatal casualties in dwellings and about 34% of the non-fatal casualties.

Table 10

Fire in Dwellings
Fatal & Non-Fatal Casualties

	FATAL	NON-FATAL
TOTALS (all causes)	653	9, 027
Clothing – On person	48	61
Clothing – Other	28	278
Bedding	132	993
Upholstery, covers	191	1,364
Floor coverings	19	160
Other furnishings & furniture	21	225
Total (all textiles)	439	3,081

2 Central Fire Brigade Advisory Council

At a meeting of the Joint Fire Prevention Committee of the Central Fire Brigades Advisory Councils concern was expressed about the difficulty of ensuring that unacceptably high fire risks were not introduced into high life hazard residential occupancies eg. old peoples homes and nursing homes. This concern was expressed against a background of intense research into the burning behaviour of furniture generally and in a number of associated fields.

3 Hazards

It is necessary, in assessing the contribution to hazard brought about by the introduction of new materials to consider the most important ways in which materials, in the fire context, can effect hazard.

It will be noted that some quite small fires, involving limited amounts of plastic material, rapidly give rise to large volumes of smoke. A fundamental difference is, that whereas the smoke from what might be considered "traditional" materials used in furnishings could be controlled or dispersed by ventilation (causing the materials to burn freely with reduced smoke production), the behaviour of the plastic materials is different in that ventilation not only increases the rate of burning but also increases the rate of smoke production.

This rapid production of dense smoke and toxic gases, means that time available for escape from the upper floors of the normal domestic dwelling may be as little as two or three minutes from the onset of flaming combustion. This partially accounts for the fact that, over recent years, the number of people requiring rescue from fires in the United Kingdom has increased substantially.

4 Furniture and furnishings

As mentioned in Chapter 11, domestic furniture in the UK is subject to Regulations (under the Consumer Safety Act) which require suppliers to label the furniture in such a way that the customer is aware whether it is capable of being ignited by a small flame eg. smokers materials. Modern upholstery usually comprises a covering material over a foam or fibrous base and, of these, the covering material is probably the more important as regards ignition.

Some combinations are particularly easily ignited. One combination has been shown to be capable of achieving flashover conditions within 4 or 5 minutes of being ignited by a small source eg. a match.

Other man-made fibres are also known to have a fast propagation of flame whereas others eg. nylon will only char. Other natural materials, such as cotton, will smoulder. Both natural and synthetic Latex foam, as used in beds and mattresses, can also be ignited by a small source and burn with a great deal of black smoke and heat. It can also produce "cold smoke" which has been known to cause explosions especially at domestic fires.

5 Floor coverings

Although firefighters do not, usually, expect floor coverings to contribute to a fire in a normal domestic fire, some modern carpets can.

If a normal wool carpet, is subjected to a small source of ignition, the flame would not be expected to spread very far from the source. Other carpets, however, may be comprised of modacrylic, acrylic or propylene piles on a foam base. Some modacrylic fibres are resistant to the spread of flame and they are often added to acrylic piles to reduce an otherwise high fire hazard.

Various other types of fibres are used eg. polyethylene which are easily ignitable, but it has been suggested that the main hazard is the foam backing on which the fibres are laid.

6 Other internal hazards

Mention was made, in the Introduction, to polystyrene tiles which can be, and are, laid on ceilings and walls usually by the DIY enthusiast. Unfortunately, they are seldom put up correctly ie. the adhesive is seldom applied all over the underside and they are too often painted. The consequence is a very rapid surface spread of flame, the tiles form flaming droplets or just drop, flaming, to the floor.

Plastics are used in the form of mouldings in a wide variety of places, and a thin polystyrene wall veneer which is either painted or has wallpaper stuck onto it is another hazard which can cause rapid surface spread of flame.

Rigid polyurethane ceilings are also to be found. Their fire resistance can be low and penetration into a roof void could take place very quickly following ignition.

7 Fire Precautions Act 1971

Since the introduction of the Fire Precautions Act 1971, significant developments have taken place in the recognition of the fire risks associated with the contents of buildings. The Act anticipated such developments because, written into it, are several references to the contents of premises and these include a direct reference to furniture. Section 6(2) of the Act sets out the requirements which may be imposed by a Fire Certificate if the Fire Authority consider them appropriate in the circumstances.

Such requirements may provide for means of escape to be properly maintained and kept free from obstruction, for means for fighting fire and giving warning in case of fire to be properly maintained and

"as to *other* precautions to be observed in the relevant buildings in relation to the risk, in case of fire, to persons in the premises".

It is thought that this provision could be used to impose requirements as to the flammability of textile products used along escape routes. However, in Certificates hitherto issued under the Act, Fire Authorities are not likely to have imposed such requirements because technical information about the risk associated with the burning behaviour of furniture and furnishings was not available to the extent that it is today.

Section 8(2) of the Act provides that where a Fire Certificate is in force, any proposals to change the conditions in the premises must be notified to the Fire Authority before any such work is commenced. One of the specified proposals which must be so notified is

"if it is proposed to make a material alteration in the internal arrangements of the premises or to the furniture *and equipment* with which the premises are provided".

The 1971 Act therefore does allow such factors as the fire behaviour of textile products to be taken into account in the determination of means of escape requirements and other requirements which may be incorporated in Fire Certificates. In this connection, it is of interest that Section 12 of the Act enables the Secretary of State to make Regulations as to fire precautions in the case of any particular premises which he has the power to designate under the Act. Such Regulations may impose requirements,

"as to the internal construction of the premises and the materials used in that construction"

and also,

"for prohibiting altogether the presence or use in the premises of furniture or equipment of any specified description, or prohibiting its presence or use unless specified standards or conditions are complied with".

8 Fire tests

Chapter 2 describes fire testing carried on in the UK under BS476. These tests, however, are are all directed towards the elements of structure of buildings rather than their contents. Chapter 11 lists most of the relevant British Standards which apply to fabrics, upholstery, bedding furniture, beds, drapes etc. It also includes references to the various Home Office Guides and Codes of Practice.

Chapter 11
Guidance in respect of contents of buildings

1 General

Public buildings can usually be taken as buildings of larger volume, containing larger amounts of furniture and furnishings and accommodating, either temporarily or semi-permanently, large numbers of people.

The study of fire growth in domestic size rooms may have a relevance to certain public buildings eg. small hotels, old peoples homes and nursing homes.

What has to be borne in mind is that different standards must prevail for different risks. A material which is deemed suitable for the environment of fully mobile people may, because of its characteristics, not be deemed suitable for people who cannot move away from a fire unaided or, in special circumstances, are restrained from doing so eg. locked wards of mental hospitals. In other words, the risk involved is also a function of the occupancy.

Certain furniture, for example, may contain a material that is easily ignited but is encased in something which is more resistant to fire. If this was placed in a public place where there is a chance of vandalism and the outer cover was to be damaged the combustible material could be exposed and the chance of ignition increased.

2 Home Office guidelines

A fundamental requirement of fire safety legislation is that a *reasonable* level of safety in the event of fire should be provided. The Home Office guides listed below have no statutory force. They are intended to provide guidance to those responsible for planning fire precautions in such premises. They are intended for both those persons responsible for the day-to-day running of the premises as well as those persons with an enforcement/inspectorial role.

The following lists those published or planned and illustrates the type of buildings to which they apply:

Existing:

(i) Guide to Fire Precautions in Existing Places of Work that Require a Fire Certificate.

(ii) Code of Practice for Fire Precautions in Factories, Offices, Shops and Railway Premises not required to have a Fire Certificate.

(iii) Guide to Fire Precautions in Hospitals.

(iv) Guide to Fire Precautions in Existing Residential Care Premises.

(v) Guide to Fire Precautions in Existing Places of Entertainment and Like Premises.

(vi) Guide to Fire Precautions in Existing Hotels and Boarding Houses that Require a Fire Certificate.

(vii) Fire Safety Management in Hotels and Boarding Houses.

Proposed:–

(i) Guide to the Cinemas (Safety) Regulations 19__*

   * Depends on passing on Cinemas (Safety) Regulations and is subject to redrafting to bring into line with the Entertainments Guide.

3 Advice to Fire Officers and purchasers

The following extracts from the Guidance Documents illustrates the relevant advice given to Fire Officers when inspecting premises to issue fire certificates and also to those responsible for the provision of contents of these premises.

   Extract from **"Guide to Fire Precautions in Existing Places of Work that require a Fire Certificate: Factories, Offices, Shops and Railway Premises."**

Advice on furniture and furnishings.

Para 12.7
Furniture and furnishings which are easily ignited or demonstrate rapid spread of flame characteristics present a particular fire hazard and their presence will be a factor in determining the acceptability of escape routes and in particular of protected routes.

Para 12.8
It should be noted that furniture sold for use in industrial or commercial premises is not required to comply with the provisions of the Furniture and Furnishings (Fire) (Safety) Regulations 1988.

Extract from **"Guide to Fire Precautions in Hospitals."**

Furniture and furnishings – flammability."

Para 2.63
In addition to the measures suggested for the surfaces of walls and ceilings etc. it will be necessary also to see that no undue risk is

114

presented by the unavoidable use of furniture and furnishings which are dangerously combustible or have unnecessarily flammable surfaces".

Extract from **"Guide to Fire Precautions in Existing Residential Care Premises Furniture and furnishings – flammability."**

Para 2.59
The use of furniture or furnishings that are easily ignited or demonstrate rapid spread of surface flame characteristics should be avoided.

Extract from **"Guide to Fire Precautions in Existing Places of Entertainment and Like Premises."**

Advice on furniture and furnishings and synthetic materials

Para 4.12 Furniture and furnishings which are easily ignited or demonstrate rapid spread of flame characteristics present a particular fire hazard and their presence will be a factor in determining the acceptability of escape routes and in particular of protected routes.

Upholstered furniture

Para 4.14
Application for consent for upholstered furniture should, where required, be made to the licensing authority in writing and should be accompanied by full details of the materials to be used and a certificate from an approved testing establishment. The licensing authority may, after consideration of specific circumstances of use, vary the level of ignition source which seating is required to meet.

Para 4.15 All fixed and movable seating should be maintained free from tears, rips etc. which would result in the filling being exposed.

Extract from the **"Guide to the Fire Precautions in premises used as Hotels and Boarding Houses which require a Fire Certificate. "**

Chapter 19 complete.

Extract from **"Fire Safety Management in Hotels and Boarding Houses."**

Chapter 7 (g) Floor Coverings, Furniture, Furnishings, Beds and Bedding
The fibre and cellular foam fillings in most upholstered furniture and beds are easily ignited by cigarettes and matches. Staff should therefore check regularly that there are no tears or rips which have resulted in the filling material being exposed.

When refurbishment or replacement of floor coverings, furniture and furnishings, beds and bedding takes place care should be taken to ensure that the materials chosen conform to the relevant British Standard. This is especially important in the case of beds and bedding as it should be remembered that despite any warnings to the contrary, many people do smoke in bed.

Note: In smaller premises (eg. those which do not require a fire certificate) furniture which meets the current requirements for domestic furniture will often be used, but it should be noted that its resistance to ignition is likely to be less than that designed for commercial use.

4 British Standards:

a. Ignition sources

Mention is made in the following Standards of various ignition sources. These range from 0 to 7 in increasing severity and are those specified in BS 5852. Briefly, they may be described as:

Ignition source 0   a smouldering cigarette

Ignition sources 1 - 3   gas flames of increasing severity and

Ignition sources 4 - 7   timber cribs of increasing mass.

b. Furniture and Furnishings.

These should conform to British Standard 5852 ignition source 0 and ignition source 5.

Note: There could be an area within a hotel, such as a basement disco, where an increased performance criteria such as ignition source 7, instead of ignition source 5, could be required. All furniture should contain only those filling materials approved by the **Furniture and Furnishing (Fire) (Safety) Regulations** and the **Furniture and Furnishings (Fire) (Safety)(Amendment) Regulations.**

Note: These standards are subject to periodic amendment in the light of proposed European legislation on furniture.

c. Floor coverings.

These should be tested to British Standard 4790 and classified as low radius of fire spread in accordance with British Standard 5827. BS 4569 and 6307 also apply and tests are mounted according to whether the covering is to be "looselaid", "fully adhered" or "loose-laid with underlay".

d. Beds and Bedding.

These should be tested to British Standard 6807: section 3 and the composite of the bedding materials should resist ignition sources 0 and 5.

e. Curtains and Drapes.

These should conform to British Standard 5867, both surface and edge ignition, and be classified as Type "B".

Extract from **"Draft Guide to the Cinemas (Safety) Regulations 19__ "**.

Upholstered furniture

Upholstered seating furniture should satisfy, as a minimum standard, the Cigarette and Match Ignitability Test specified in British Standard 5852: Part 1 and a level of crib ignition specified in source 5 of British Standard 5852: Part 2. However, it should be noted that British Standard 5852 does not test the resistance to ignition of the underside of the seating.

Part 5
Examples of buildings

Having described materials and building components in previous Parts, in this Part an attempt is made to explain how they come together, with fire safety in mind, in the design of buildings.

Building Regulations stipulate standards of construction and are aimed at the safety of people and of enhancing their chances of escaping from a building on fire without injury. They also seek to prevent or limit fire spread inside a building and from one building to another.

The increasing complexity and size of buildings today where, in some cases, literally thousands of people work or resort to, poses many problems. An example of this is a town centre development. This may include department stores, shops, offices, hotels, car parks, restaurants, theatres, a leisure centre, indoor and outdoor markets and multi-level walkways. To make this type of environment safe yet workable architects, building control officers and fire prevention officers etc. have to plan carefully.

Because of their good record so far, there is little information as to how one of these complexes does react to a fire. However, fires have occurred and have highlighted some problems eg. reverse flow of smoke, failure of smoke detectors and/or sprinklers to operate due to unforeseen smoke or heat barriers. This has caused a rethink in design and, in some cases, alterations to legislation and practical guidance which, in turn will affect future designs.

Large complexes and buildings are often now designed as "intelligent" constructions. This means, usually, that there is a central control room which monitors all the systems in the building including those exclusively used for fire safety.

It must be borne in mind that quite a few buildings are designed for "general" use and it is the occupier who decides on its final internal layout. Alternatively, buildings are designed for a particular use but the first occupier moves out, the use changes but the "particular" design does not. This can cause headaches for the fire prevention officer and the firefighter. In the Building Regulations the purposes for which buildings are used (or intended to be used in the case of proposed buildings) are divided into "purpose" or "occupancy" groups. These groupings reflect the potential hazard that is expected to exist in relation to the safety of people likely to resort to the premises, and to the fireload ie. the amount of combustible material present. At the top of the groupings are residential and institutional buildings which have a sleeping risk. In a lot of cases this situation is worsened by the fact that some occupants find it difficult to move without assistance.

The scale continues through to buildings used for storage where the fire damage potential may be high but the life risk is relatively low. All groups take safety of people into consideration. Amongst many things, the regulations limit the size of the buildings in relation to the period of fire resistance of its elements of structure (see Chapter 4). Having determined the potential hazard of the use of the building, the Regulations seek to ensure that it has sufficient fire resistance to prevent (a) a major collapse and (b) a large scale fire. In these chapters examples of buildings will be given according to these groupings but, as there are so many variations in each group, only a representative selection is made. The Regulations apply to;

(i)   new buildings

(ii)   structural alterations or extensions to existing buildings (irrespective of when the building was erected)

(iii) to certain works or fittings (including replacements) eg. drains, incinerators

(iv)   when a material change of use is deemed to have been proposed.

Firefighters still have to consider buildings erected before the introduction of the Regulations which are, often, comparatively sub-standard to those erected now. Examples are given, as far as possible, of both "old" and "new" buildings used for similar purposes

Chapter 12
Residential and institutional buildings

1 Terraced and semi-detached houses

Older types of terraced housing have the outer walls and the separating walls of brick or stone. The internal walls are more commonly of wooden studding faced each side with lath and plaster. The internal walls often carry part of the weight of the floors which span between them and either the outer or separating walls. The wooden floor joists have boarding on top and lath and plaster or plasterboard ceilings underneath. The roof is usually constructed of timber and is tiled or slated. Virtually the whole interior of this type of house is constructed of timber and fire spread can be rapid.

These houses are often sub-divided into flats and tenements, the resulting overcrowding increasing the risk to life. Means of escape can often be inadequate and access to the rear of the building difficult, if not impossible.

There is a **"Guide to Means of escape and related fire safety measures in certain houses in multiple occupation"** (HMOs) which gives advice on how to alleviate these problems.

Modern terraced housing, sometimes of 3 or 4 floors, is now called "town-housing". The ground floor is often a garage with the living rooms on the first floor and the bedrooms above. Construction varies but floors of 22mm sheet plywood on timber joists are not unusual plus a bituminous felt on timber flat roof. In most cases the imperforate separating walls are taken through the roof by at least 375mm to prevent fire spread between occupancies.

A problem arises in old terraced housing where, sometimes, the separating walls are only carried up to the top ceiling level leaving a "common" roof void running the whole length of the terrace. If fire penetrates the top ceiling anywhere in the terrace it can spread through the roof space and down into other occupancies.

Semi-detached houses of the older type can have the same problems because of similar construction. Roof construction in modern types has become very light in cross-sectional area and any involvement can lead to rapid spread of fire and collapse.

2 Flats and maisonettes

a. Flats

For all practical purposes the term "flat" means a dwelling forming part of a large block with common access which has all its habitable rooms and kitchen on one level or, in the case of "split-level flats", not more than half a storey apart. Purpose built flats are, generally, of more than two storeys and are referred to as "multi-storey", "high-point" or "tower blocks".

b. Maisonettes

A maisonette differs from a flat in that, although it forms part of a larger block with common access, its habitable rooms and kitchen are divided between two, or more, levels which are more than half a storey apart.

The design of maisonettes varies greatly. There are the simple type approached from a common open balcony or deck with living rooms at entrance level and bedrooms on the floor above.

Firefighters, however, will find more complex interlocking forms through two or more floors with living rooms and bedrooms on any floor and possibly two entrances at different levels.

c. Means of escape

BS 5588 Part 1 specifically deals with the protection of the occupants of flats and maisonettes, the means of escape, the construction of the building and the equipment necessary for preventing the rapid spread of fire.

The concept of the use of manipulative apparatus for means of escape or the external rescue using Fire Service ladders is no longer acceptable. The protection must be designed and built into the building with adequate fire resistance between dwellings, limits on travel distances, alternative means of escape etc.

Fig. 12.1 gives a simplified example of alternative means of escape from a flat. Any route from the staircase to an external door at ground, or podium, level is regarded as an extension of the staircase and must be protected accordingly.

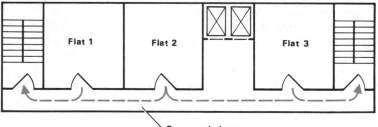

Fig. 12.1 Layout showing a number of maisonettes with a common balcony escape route to staircases at the end.

3 Timber-framed houses

Many old timber-framed houses remain and are usually constructed of stout timbers with an infill of brick noggin or plaster. Internally the floors are often of heavy timbers as is the roof which can be tiled, slated or thatched. The numerous concealed spaces brought about by centuries of alterations make any fire in this type of building particularly difficult and dangerous.

Timber-framed houses have, in the last 20 years, experienced a resurgence but the construction is very different.

The main framing is of light timbers with very light roof trusses. A great deal of prefabrication is used and the trusses are, sometimes, of only 40mm finished thickness and they are not nailed or screwed but held together by different types of metal connector plates (see Fig. 5.10).

The house frame walls are completed by prefabricated panels of plasterboard sheathed with plywood or fibreboards. These, in turn, are covered with a membrane which acts as a breathing weather protection. This membrane can be made of chemically waterproofed Kraft paper or bitumen-treated paper. As both of these can be easily ignited the tendency is to use a thermoplastic sheeting which will shrink away from a heat source instead of igniting. The whole frame is then clad in brickwork.

Ground floors usually consist of a concrete slab with timber or plastic flooring laid directly onto it. There is a move back to the raised type of ventilated timber ground floor with services running under. Upper floors can be of 12-13mm planks on rafters or, in some cases, plywood sheeting on timber rafters, both underdrawn by plasterboard ceilings.

Firefighters should be aware that some ceilings may conceal a heating system. This could be a low temperature radiant system where the heating elements are built into the ceiling often by stapling the current carrying metal foil to the underside of the joists or battens.

In the one system the metal foil is embedded in a strong plastic sheet, the total thickness being about 0.2mm. The elements provide about $200W/m^2$ from the normal voltage of 220/240. Plasterboard would then be erected in the normal way leaving no obvious indication of the presence of the heating system.

Modern installations should be provided with an Earth Leakage Circuit Breaker (ELCB) or a Residual Current Circuit Breaker (RCCB) which are to set to trip out if the system is damaged.

Firefighters should question the occupant if they have any suspicion that this sort of system is fitted and take all the normal precautions as when dealing with live electrical circuits.

Insulation, both in the roof and walls, is currently mineral fibre (rock or glass) but expanded polystyrene and expanded polythene are permitted.

From a fire-spread point of view, providing the appropriate firestopping has been correctly installed and the construction is good, fires can be contained. Unfortunately, however, this type of construction does engender numerous cavities and, if the fire breaks through into these, spread can then be rapid and largely unseen (see Chapter 4(3b).

The large amount of lightweight timber surface area in the roof also means a rapid spread if the fire penetrates into the roof space. Another factor to be borne in mind is that the metal fasteners/connectors have been known to expand and fall out of the timber trussing in a fire situation leaving the clay tile roof unsupported and causing rapid collapse. Firefighters should be aware of this trend in construction and be wary of climbing onto any of these roofs which have suffered internal fire damage.

4 Hotels

Hotels come within the "other residential" user group of buildings for the purpose of the Building Regulations and it is these regulations which limit the floor area and cubic capacity if each storey or compartment.

In general, the design of hotels is such that the lower floors contain the amenities eg. ballroom/conference area, bars, restaurant and kitchens. Upper floors are given over to bedrooms and suites.

These arrangements depend often, of course, on the peculiarities of that particular site. The advent of atria, large expanses of glass or polycarbonates, roof gardens, energy conservation ideas etc. has lead to completely new designs (see Plate 13 and Fig. 12.2).

In some buildings the traditional position has been reversed with the amenities on the upper floors and the suites below. This can add to the problems of means of escape whereby the largest numbers of people will be the farthest from safety and has led to a great deal of new thinking on the interpretation of the Building Regulations.

Fig. 12.2 An example of a floor plan in a large modern hotel.

"The Fire Precautions Act, 1971" was enacted to enable fire authorities to require reasonable measures to be taken in hotels, and similar premises, to protect people using these premises. Recently an up-dated **"Guide to fire precautions in existing hotels and boarding houses"** has been issued aimed at those premises requiring a fire certificate. This was necessary because the **"Fire Safety and Safety at places of Sport Act, 1987"** amended the 1971 Act giving additional powers to fire authorities and additional requirements.

To assist owners and managers of these types of premises, the Home Departments, together with the Fire Protection Association, have issued a guide **"Fire Safety Management in Hotels and Boarding Houses"**.

Firefighters must bear in mind that the majority of people in hotels are there for the first time, are almost totally unaware of the general layout of the floors, exits etc., do not absorb the printed fire instructions in their rooms and are generally disorientated, at least for a time. Under fire conditions this can be, and too often is, fatal.

The design of hotels, the fire prevention measures incorporated and the general requirements of the 1971 Act all attempt to redress this situation but the more the local firefighter knows about the premises the greater the chance of success in any firefighting or rescues.

5 Institutional buildings

a. General

This designation includes buildings used as hospitals, community homes, boarding schools and similar establishments where persons in need of care sleep on the premises. No specific type of building covers these establishments which can be converted country mansions; large private houses quite often used as private nursing homes; single and two storey modular built units used as old persons homes right through to multi-storey, steel-framed hospitals.

b. Fire precautions

The greater life-risk in these premises is recognised in the Building Regulations and the requirements for new and converted buildings are very stringent. The DHSS issued **Health Technical Memoranda (HTMs)** and **Fire Codes** covering requirements for new non-nucleus hospitals, new hospital extensions and major alterations. There is also considerable guidance on the design of "nucleus" hospitals and **Draft Guides** on fire precautions in (a) hospitals and (b) existing residential care premises which includes privately run establishments. All District Health Authorities were authorised, in 1971, to appoint specialist FPOs in order to have expert advice on bringing their premises up to acceptable standards of fire prevention and fire protection and most have done this.

c. Nucleus hospitals

In 1975 the hospital planning authorities started a programme of standardising new hospitals on what is known as the "nucleus" design. This, in itself, is a development of a module method called "Harness" which was introduced in 1971. The principles and recommendations for the safety of the occupants in the event of fire were laid down in HTM **"Fire and Safety in Health Buildings, 1978".**

From the fire precautions point of view a design can be regarded as "standard nucleus" as long as the following are not varied.

(i)   two/three storeys

(ii) Fire compartmentation
The plans for each phase should contain a minimum of two adjoining compartments ie. cruciform templates, per floor linked to the hospital "street" (minimum 3 modules long with 2 staircases).

NB. Each clinical cruciform template is approx $1000m^3$. The "street" is a minimum of 3m wide.
A nucleus hospital of about 300 beds would comprise of 14 templates, probably on 2 floors with a 2 storey services zone (see Fig 12.3).

(iii) Fire sub-compartmentation

(iv) Escape routes and travel distances

(v)   Building and engineering principles

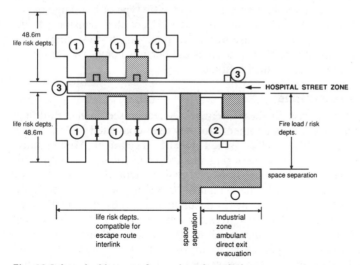

Fig. 12.3 A typical layout of a nucleus hospital.
The major components of Nucleus design example 1 are:-
① Cruciform shape clinical template is a standard fire compartment
② Service block as a fire compartment with separation from ①
③ Hospital street zone with service ducts and vertical communication shafts stairs/lifts in courtyards.

Eventually the use of the nucleus design on existing hospital sites plus the need to co-ordinate nucleus and whole-hospital policies generated the need for additional spaces for supporting accommodation in association with standard cruciform templates. This meant that a new component had to be introduced into nucleus allowing small units of space between templates and the hospital "street". These have become known as "pods". Fig. 12.4 illustrates how these pods fit into the front of standard templates.

In the light of experience development of the original concept has taken place. Fig 12.5 shows an example of a 600 bed nucleus hospital. The extended clinical templates (1a) are limited by the travel distances to the "street". Where they exceed the permitted distance alternative means of escape have to be provided.

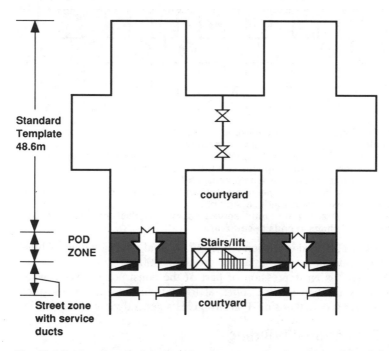

Fig. 12.4 Nucleus hospital design showing example of position of "pods".

The courtyards themselves provide adequate space separation, light etc. but must not be used for "pods". All ducting, lifts, shafts etc. have to form fire-resisting compartments to standard and there must be adequate fire separation between the "street" and other compartments.

Access for fire appliances is another factor which is borne in mind and the requirements depend on the volume of the building (m^3) which is over 9m in height.

Fig. 12.6 shows a general floor plan of an actual nucleus designed hospital. There is room, and plans, to add another two templates to the North of the complex replacing older buildings.

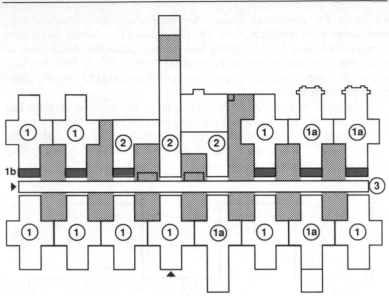

Fig. 12.5 Typical layout of a 600 bed nucleus hospital.
The major components of Nucleus design.
① Cruciform shape clinical template as a standard fire compartment.
  ⑩ Extended clinical templates as a fire compartment
  ⑪ Accommodation pods (see paragraph #)
② Support service L shape templates and deep plan departments a fire compartments with space separation.
③ Hospital street zone with service ducts, vertical connections with protected shafts in pods or courtyards.

This is a 200 bed extension to the old hospital and, including all other facilities and the wards, has a total area of 17000m².

Fig. 12.7 is an impression of part of the construction over a ward. The walk through service spine, at top left in the apex of the roof, serves wards on either side. Plate 14 gives a general view of the site.

6 Educational buildings

a. General

The term educational buildings covers a wide range of buildings from the village school to large university complexes. From the 1st April 1991 all educational buildings came under the Building Regulations. Before this date they were exempt and were only subject to the Education (Schools and Further Education) Regulations and any of the bulletins issued in respect of the Regulations. Guidance in respect of fire precautions is given in Building Bulletin No. 7 (BB7) for new primary and secondary day schools.

b. Other uses

Whilst the fire precautions recommended in BB7 may be adequate for

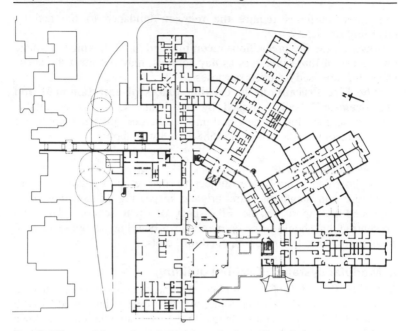

Fig. 12.6 General floor plan of a nucleus designed hospital.

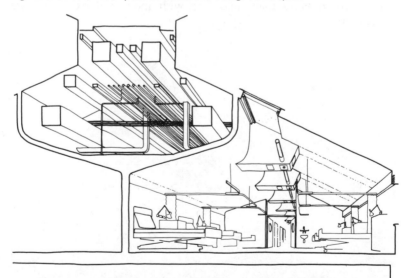

Fig. 12.7 A cross-section of a Ward and the service spine above, in the hospital shown in Fig 12.6 and Plate 14.

these buildings when they are used as day schools they may not meet the needs when the buildings are used for other activities.

Schools are beginning to be looked upon as a community resource eg. for evening classes, clubs, entertainment and sports centres. These, and other, purposes require the relevant guidance to the activity regarding fire safety.

However, the fire precautions recommended in BB7, whilst adequate for the use of those premises as day schools, may not meet the needs when they are used for other purposes.

"The Fire Precautions in existing places of entertainment and like premises" booklet issued by the Home Office is a suitable advisory source. But, for new buildings at the design stage compliance with the recommendations of BS5588 Part 8 will apply.

c. Boarding schools

Many boarding schools are subject to inspection by the DES for suitability and standards. Fire brigade inspecting officers are often requested to report on the FP aspect of such schools. The Fire Prevention that should be recommended for boarding school residential areas is similar to that recommended for hotels.

d. Modular systems of school building

In the 1950s and 1960s a number of local authorities cooperated in modular systems of school building, two examples being called CLASP and SCOLA. These systems adhered to the recommendations laid down by BB7 but the buildings themselves have been extensively modified since then to bring them into line with modern thinking on fire precautions.

Chapter 13
Commercial and industrial stores

1 Shops and departmental stores

The term "shop" covers, virtually, an unlimited range of premises from the small shop on the corner to the largest hypermarket or departmental store.

The problems created by all but the smallest shops led to the "Offices, Shops and Railway premises Act, 1963 (OSRA) which gave fire authorities some powers to require a degree of fire protection for the public. New buildings are governed by the Building Regulations which, among other things, aims to restrict the extent of the open floor areas and cubic capacity of the building and/or compartment within the building.

The present standard is directed towards the safety of life by:

(i)   planning escape routes

(ii) planning to prevent the spread of fire

(iii) constructing and finishing with non-hazardous materials and embodying adequate fire resistance into the structures

(iv) segregating the high-risk areas eg. selling areas from the non-selling areas ie. stores, loading bays, receiving and despatch departments etc.

For selling, the contents of shops are often displayed in such a way as to enhance fire spread, impede the movement of firefighters and create the maximum heat and smoke in the shortest possible time. This often delays close tackling of the fire which gives it time to affect the structure.

One aspect of which firefighters should be aware is that many small shops are conversions from former private houses. This was often carried by placing a steel joist across what is now the shop window area to support the upper walls. Frequently it has been found that these are not suitably protected against fire with the possibility of the collapse of the complete front of the building.

Where towns do not have new shopping complex specially built they sometimes develop old covered markets and glaze over the surrounding narrow streets. Fire protection measures are, obviously, looked at with care but the reaction of these older parts of the town to fire can never be accurately assessed and firefighters, again, should be vigilant when tackling fires in this type of area. These mixed hazards are highlighted in BS 5588.

2 Offices

This type of occupancy can be found almost anywhere and of any construction often as part of another sort of occupancy. Design guidance for new office buildings or alterations to existing buildings is contained in BS5588 Part 3, 1983. This makes specific recommendations on fire protection, number and position of exits, prevention of fire spread and general fire precautions.

New office buildings include, among other things, atria, large areas of glass or polycarbonates, curtain walling, cladding of various types, wall climbing lifts and whole floors given over to services (see Plates 16, 17, 18 and 19).

To accommodate the mass of electronic technology many buildings will have "access" floors ie. raised floors giving access to cables, ducting etc.

Not least important are the numbers of people who work or resort to these buildings. A complete evacuation of a 25/30 storey office block could take an hour so they are designed with compartmentation to a high degree of resistance to fire and smoke spread and protection to the means of escape. Fig. 13.1 illustrates the sort of plan which could accompany a fire certificate for one floor of an office building. The degree of protection is selfevident.

Many office blocks are now designed as "intelligent" buildings eg. all services controlled by computers with, usually, a control room somewhere in the complex fully manned 24 hours a day. Firefighters will know of this location and be assisted by the numerous visual and audible displays.

A new factor which is arising, particularly in office blocks, is the provision of access and means of escape for disabled people. BS 5588 Part 8, 1988 and the Building Regulations both discuss and recommend appropriate standards. These are additional factors which the management and the Fire Service must take into consideration.

3 Airport complexes.

This type of complex is hard to define. The larger airports are so diverse in the facilities they provide and deal with such vast numbers of people that they are commercial, industrial and places to which the public resort together on a grand scale.

They present a particular headache to Fire Prevention Officers with the confluence of people, aircraft, highly flammable fuel, shops, malls etc. Their design varies but great care is taken to make them as safe as possible within the Building Regulations. Fig. 13.2 (bottom) is a cross-sectional drawing of part of Stansted Airport and gives some idea of the public areas. Fig. 13.2 (top) is a projection of one of the satellites and shows the movement areas and services.

LEGEND

WR   WET RISER OUTLET

O   EMERGENCY LIGHT

⊙   FIRE ALARM CALL POINT

🇪   EXIT SIGN WITH DIRECTIONAL ARROW

SK   FLOOR PROTECTED BY SPRINKLERS

VP   VISION PANEL

SC   SELF CLOSING FIRE RESISTING DOOR

▽W   9 LITRE WATER EXTINGUISHERS

▨   FIRE HOSE

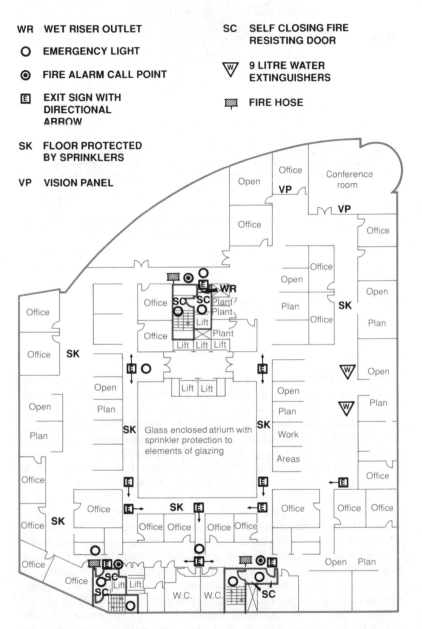

Fig. 13.1 Example of the type of floor plan in an office block which would accompany a fire certificate.

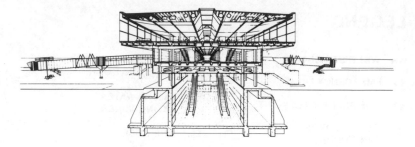

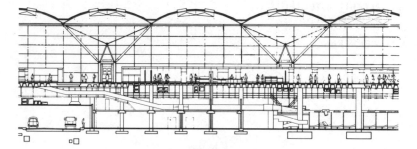

Fig. 13.2 (top) An airport satellite area in cross-section.
(bottom) Cross-section of part of Stansted airport.

4 Industrial buildings

During the 19thC a large number of manufactories were built and many are still standing although almost all are not used for their original purpose Fig. 9.1 illustrates a typical construction of that period.

Today many new factories appear to be constructed on the single storey principle with large internal dimensions with perhaps a mezzanine floor for various service departments eg. offices, stores, drawing sections. Some will have these facilities in a 2/3 storey block at one end with a large single storey factory building attached.

Many factories and storage facilities are being built using a light frame of steel or precast concrete covered in steel, or other alloy, sheets. These sheets are the outer skin enclosing a "sandwich" of polyisocyanurate or polyurethane foamed plastic covered internally with either another metal sheet or commercial board (Fig. 13.3). These "sandwich" sheets are often specially designed to be attached, in blocks, to the frame and to make a continuous wall and roof (see Fig. 5.16) the ends of the building being enclosed by similar sheeting.

Most industrial layouts work on the principle of access for raw materials, processing through the plant with a final destination for finished commodities either into store or onto the dispatch bay for delivery.

Fig. 13.3 A typical "sandwich" sheet used to make up the "skin" of a building.

Although many of the older multi-storey factories still use the top-to-ground system, the single storey floor system seems to be prevalent.

The dangers of the top-to-ground system are found in the multitude of openings between storeys to accommodate various power transmissions, chutes, ducts, conveyors, systems etc. The dangers of the single storey system lies in the, sometimes, vast open areas which are found under one roof an example being in vehicle manufacture. Obviously, high risk areas such as spray booths and flammable goods stores must be strictly segregated by fire-resisting structures. A simplified layout of such a factory is shown in Fig. 13.4.

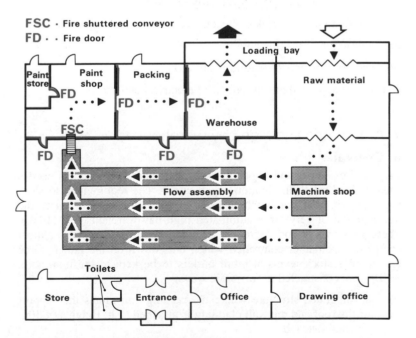

Fig. 13.4. A simple diagram of a factory layout.

5 Cold stores

These buildings are, usually, particularly difficult for access as their design is geared to preserving low temperatures by substantial insulation (itself, if of the old type, a fire hazard) and restricted internal and external openings. They are often built of a monolithic reinforced concrete frame infilled with brick or concrete blocks, the whole being "double-skinned". These are sub-divided internally into large compartments which are, themselves, "double-skinned". Additional hazards to firefighters are either the release of refrigerants during a fire or the spread of fire within the double-skin. These, and other salient points are discussed in the Manual Part 6c, Section 12 "Refrigeration plant risks".

6 Spirit Storage

A particular example of a storage building requiring special consideration is that containing whisky in bulk. Guidance has been issued on the design of new single storey buildings used for spirit storage in the Fire Prevention Guide No. 2/1973. Attention is drawn to:

(i)   limitation of compartment size

(ii) light roof construction to vent any explosion

(iii) installation of a sprinkler system

(iv) restriction of racking height

(v)   specific amounts of natural ventilation

(vi) use of approved intrinsically safe electrical equipment.

7 Automated and high-bay warehouses

a. General

Large stores, super and hyper markets and other retail outlets need a sophisticated retail distribution organisation. The requirement to store huge quantities of goods which have a rapid turnover has led to the development of very large automated high-bay warehouses (AHBW). These vary in size and degree of automation but the latest are almost completely computer controlled which cuts down on the labour force and enables stock levels at retail outlets to be kept to the minimum. AHBW are constructed in two basic ways:

(i)   an integrated structure where the racking constitutes the support for the roof and the wall cladding is attached to it. Heights of 30m are common, and

(ii) where the racking is separate from, and does not support, the walls and roof. These tend to be smaller probably up to about 15m high.

The floor areas and cubic capacity are large. Some dimensions and a brief description of one such building are as follows:

High bay building

155m x 55m x 22m	cubic capacity	187550m³
	floor area	8525m²
Total pallet storage	11 high x 24 wide x 112 long =	
		29, 568 pallets
No. of cranes	6 = 4, 928 pallets/crane	
(fully automatic		
computer driven)		
Throughput	Up to 3 pallets/min or 2 pallets	
	in and 2 out per min, simultaneously.	
Mass of racking and		
stock	40, 000t	
Air conditioning	Temp. 13°	63% humidity.

The building is Portal framed with walls comprising 50mm steel/isocyanurate/steel composite cladding and a very low pitched roof of similar insulated material.

Low-bay area

Apart from the cranes the whole stock is moved on computer controlled conveyors to and from road and rail unloading and dispatching bays which cover another 3500m² of low bay floor area.

b. Fire protection

Automatic protection in this particular building is of a high standard. There are a large number of smoke and rate-of-rise detectors arranged in zones. The main indicator board for the system is in the works fire brigade station.

There are 6 large smoke vents at each end of the HBW and 9 of the roof trussings are enclosed in steel sheeting to act as smoke curtains.

Apart from hose-reels and extinguishers, the main firefighting system is a specially designed sprinkler system. The sprinklers are fitted both in the roof and in-rack and are so arranged that, for example, if smoke or fire are detected at level 2, sprinklers at levels 2, 3, 4 and 5 will operate. The system is backed up by 3 pumps, 2 of which are diesel driven, and 2 very large tanks of water.

Plates 20 and 21 show external and internal views of this complex.

c. Firefighting.

As each HBW is different in construction, access, automatic protection, water supplies, numbers of people, plans passed by the local Fire Authority will differ considerably.

(i) The people actually on the premises.

If the planning of the site has been done correctly the means of escape for persons on the premises will be adequate according to the numbers likely to become involved. People could, however, still fail to evacuate in time and become missing. Searching an automatic HBW can be hazardous. Plate shows the complication at the "front end" of the racks. Depending on the system used, this can be even more complicated between racks with cables, conveyor belts, picking cranes, maintenance platforms etc. which, although stopped from operating, still present hazards.

Visits to the premises by firefighters are essential so that they have some idea of the environment they could be working in, possibly in smoke. Most AHBW have a preponderance of smoke vents but this does not rule out the possibility of smokelogging under the worst conditions. BA control at an incident would have to be of a very high standard.

(ii) Contents of HBW

The contents are so varied in the usual type of HBW supplying a supermarket or hypermarket chain that a policy of the separation of hazardous goods is usually in operation. However, there are chemical HBWs, which although being extra well protected, always present the possibility of accidents, spillages, explosions and fires. Obviously preplanning will have been carried out by the brigade and the management but, according to the type of incident, decisions will have to be made on such points as :

(a) Whether to commit BA personnel into the building if there are no people involved. This will depend somewhat on the type of construction. Early collapse could be expected if a really hot fire ensued.

(b) Chemical protection and subsequent decontamination.

(c) Type of extinguishing media to be used.

(d) Damage control – when to begin.

(e) Evacuation of people down-wind if a dangerous chemical cloud or plume of toxic smoke is emitted from the incident.

Chapter 14
Public assembly buildings and Town Centres

1 Public assembly buildings

a. General

This group comprises, amongst others, theatres, cinemas, concert halls, leisure centres, museums, art galleries, churches, schools, non-residential clubs and bingo halls.

Many of these premises will be subject to some form of licence usually issued by the local authority. Such licences generally impose terms, conditions and restrictions relative to fire safety. In most cases the local authority is required to consult with the fire authority before issuing or refusing a licence. Buildings in this group are constructed in many forms and examples of typical assembly buildings are described.

b. Theatres

The traditional theatre consists of a substantial outer wall and, internally, the seating area or auditorium is divided into separate part floors at varying levels eg. circles, balcony, gallery. Each of these has sufficient exits leading to protected staircases and to the safety of open air at ground level.

Between the auditorium and the stage are the proscenium openings. Scenery, in the form of painted fabrics, plastics, various types of curtains and other large pieces of material are stored high over the stage, some on rollers in the hanging loft or "fly gallery". This is so named because such scenic effects are termed "flown or flying" scenery. Also in the stage area are the electronic and electrical controls for lighting and sound, and other set properties ("props") which are moved into the stage area from the scene dock as required.

The fire risk in the stage area is considerable so the stage area is isolated from the auditorium by a substantial wall called the proscenium wall. Only the minimum openings are allowed in this wall one of which is the stage itself. This is protected by a fire resisting curtain, known as the "iron", and this is, itself, protected by a curtain drencher system (see Fig. 14.1). Roof ventilators, in the form of haystack lantern lights (Fig. 14.1), are installed over the stage area for the rapid automatic clearance of smoke.

Many modern theatres/concert halls do not use flying scenery and their stages are not separated from the auditorium. These are called "open stage" or "theatre-in-the-round. Stage sets in this type of theatre are inherently of low combustibility or durably flameproofed. The potential fire risk is a lot less than that encountered in the traditional

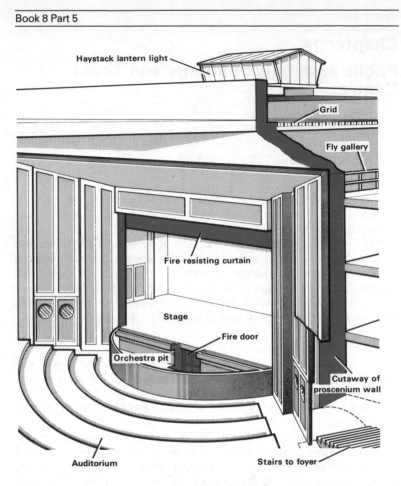

Fig. 14.1 Diagram of a traditional small stage theatre showing separation between auditorium and stage area.

"picture-frame" type of theatre. Methods of presentation are being continuously developed and the design of theatres and the conditions of licence under which they operate are adapted to the varying methods of production (see Plates 24 and 25 and Fig 14.2).

The safety of the audience is still the paramount consideration.

c. Cinemas

The older type of cinema, of which there are still a few, were constructed in a similar way to theatres and controlled in a similar way. The trend, nowadays, is for the multi-auditoria cinema and this has raised problems.

If the cinema is one of the new, purpose built single storey, multi-auditoria type then the means of escape from all auditoria are straight to open air.

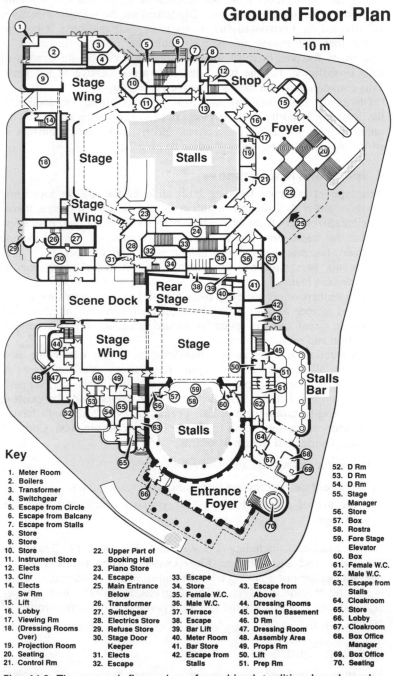

Ground Floor Plan

10 m

Key

1. Meter Room
2. Boilers
3. Transformer
4. Switchgear
5. Escape from Circle
6. Escape from Balcony
7. Escape from Stalls
8. Store
9. Store
10. Store
11. Instrument Store
12. Elects
13. Clnr
14. Elects Sw Rm
15. Lift
16. Lobby
17. Viewing Rm
18. (Dressing Rooms Over)
19. Projection Room
20. Seating
21. Control Rm

22. Upper Part of Booking Hall
23. Piano Store
24. Escape
25. Main Entrance Below
26. Transformer
27. Switchgear
28. Electrics Store
29. Refuse Store
30. Stage Door Keeper
31. Elects
32. Escape

33. Escape
34. Store
35. Female W.C.
36. Male W.C.
37. Terrace
38. Escape
39. Bar Lift
40. Meter Room
41. Bar Store
42. Escape from Stalls

43. Escape from Above
44. Dressing Rooms
45. Down to Basement
46. D Rm
47. Dressing Room
48. Assembly Area
49. Props Rm
50. Lift
51. Prep Rm

52. D Rm
53. D Rm
54. D Rm
55. Stage Manager
56. Store
57. Box
58. Rostra
59. Fore Stage Elevator
60. Box
61. Female W.C.
62. Male W.C.
63. Escape from Stalls
64. Cloakroom
65. Store
66. Lobby
67. Cloakroom
68. Box Office Manager
69. Box Office
70. Seating

Fig. 14.2 The ground floor plan of combined traditional and modern theatres under one roof.

It is the conversion of the old single auditorium cinemas to multi-auditoria that bring the problems. Dependent on the way the cinema is sub-divided eg. horizontally or vertically or, perhaps, both, it is often found that the means of escape would be either insufficient or inadequate for one, or more, of the auditoria. Perhaps the number of exits is sufficient but the travel distances are excessive or too many exits converge into one means of escape eg. one foyer.

Obviously these problems have to be resolved to the satisfaction of the licensing authority but firefighters need to know their way about the rather more complicated conversions and be aware of circumstances which may arise should an evacuation be necessary.

d. Sports and leisure centres

This type of complex is being built all over the UK in increasing numbers either as a separate entity or as part of a town centre, theme park etc. Sizes vary from what amounts to a swimming pool plus a few squash or badminton courts through to complexes which include facilities for practically every indoor sport and outdoor sport plus restaurants, bars, children's playgrounds, roofed stadia, lecture/concert halls etc (see Plate 23).

The numbers of people using these complexes at any one time can be high and include all ages. It would be difficult to restrict numbers and, therefore, great care is taken to ensure adequate fire precautions, protection and means of escape.

Construction and design are individual to a site but, being new buildings, all are subject to Building Regulations. Various pieces of legislation will apply depending on the actual use of the various parts of the complex but the **"Guide to the fire precautions in existing places of entertainment and like premises, 1990"**, although having no statutory force does direct firefighters to the relevant Acts, Codes of Practice, Guides and British Standards.

Two particular aspects are mentioned:

(i) The surface finishes and furnishings on escape routes;
(ii) the use of cellular foam eg. in gymnastic mats, and their safe storage.

British Standards including BS 476 and BS 1892 Pt. 2 and the **Furniture and Furnishings (Fire) (Safety) Regulations 1988** are relevant but are just 3 among a large number which could apply. There is also the **"Guide to safety at Sports grounds, 1990"** which advises, amongst other things, on the fire safety aspects regarding crowds of people.

2 Town Centre development

This type of building development is frequently called a "complex" and, although it may include a variety of multilevel, multi-occupancy buildings, the whole area is regarded as an entity. It can consist of a completely new environment or the conversion of an already existing area by roofing over, pedestrianisation, enclosure etc.

Some of the largest developments will occupy several acres and include a theatre/cinema/concert hall, department stores, supermarkets, open markets, leisure centres and offices. All these may be connected by podiums, escalators, bridges, galleries, staircases, wall-climbing lifts etc., and almost always include atria. Work is being carried out on BS 5588 Part 7 "Atrium Buildings" at the moment (1991) and they, together with these types of development, do present problems. Examples are shown in Plates in the Manual, Book 9.

With the prospect of the presence of large numbers of people of all ages and abilities, the means of escape is of paramount importance. Other aspects requiring thought will be access for brigade appliances, water supplies, smoke venting, sprinklers,

Modern developments of this sort are examples of "intelligent" complexes with a control room overseeing a large number of electronic devices which monitor, report and warn staff of any adverse conditions which might arise.

As with all new or materially altered buildings, these developments have to be constructed in accordance with the Building Regulations. To make a commercially viable yet reasonably safe environment architects, planners, building control officers and fire prevention officers have to work closely together.

BS 5588 Pt. 10 "Enclosed shopping complexes" deals with the subject in considerable depth.

Each development is individual and many different styles of building and building materials are used in their construction. Where possible, firefighters should take the opportunity to inspect the construction site as it progresses so that have a good knowledge of not only what will be eventually seen but much of what will be concealed.

Chapter 15
Air supported, underground and unfenestrated buildings

1 Air-supported structures

a. Types

An air-supported or pneumatic building, is generally a type of structure which consists of a single membrane anchored to the ground and kept in tension by internal air pressure so that it can support applied loading (see Fig. 1.1). The internal air pressure is maintained by a main fan or fans with provision for automatically operated standby fans. There are variations of this type of system, for example:

(i) An air-inflated structure in which air is contained within ribs formed of a membrane of PVC or other plastics or fabric. These ribs form the 'structural elements', the columns and beams which in turn support the roof and walls.

(ii) An inflated double walled structure in which air is contained between the membranes.

(iii) An air-supported structure which consists of a single membrane supported by a small pressure above atmosphere (inflation) over the whole of the structure's internal surface.

Particular designs have different characteristics from the point of view of occupant safety; for example, in the case of (iii) the designer will often incorporate lightweight steel framing for the primary purpose of

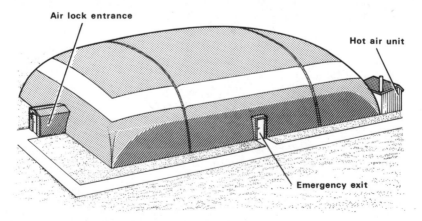

Fig. 15.1 An example of an air-supported structure.

providing a stable fixing for lighting equipment, but this may serve also to support the roof should the structure deflate for any reason.

b. Use

Air-supported structures are used in many areas because of the low capital cost and minimum maintenance costs. They are used for commercial and industrial applications, such as warehousing and manufacturing processes, for the agricultural and horticultural industries and for military use as garages, radar equipment protection, mobile hospitals and workshops. They will also be found as enclosures for swimming pools, tennis courts and other sports which are affected by adverse weather conditions.

c. Behaviour of structure in fire

The membrane, itself, can be made from either a coated fabric ie. nylon or polyester with a PVC or rubber coating or, alternatively, from plastic, PVC or polythene sheet material. BS 6661 refers to the behaviour of membranes in the event of a fire and states that the membrane should not readily support combustion. Experience has shown that PVC coated polyesters, polyamides and unreinforced polythene generally perform satisfactorily under fire conditions, melting rather than burning in a fire. Any holes formed by such melting would allow the membrane to sag with possible collapse onto the fire. Many factors are involved including the type of fabric used, the nature of jointing substance, the height and extent of the structure, and the size and type of fire.

d. Means of escape

The fundamental requirement for the safety of the public in the event of fire breaking out in any of these structures is to make sure that they quickly become aware of the danger and are able to reach a place of safety before being overcome by smoke, toxic gas or other products of fire. It is imperative therefore that every structure is provided with exits and emergency exits. BS 6661 gives guidance on the number of exits, their width, siting and travel distances. Ironically the door most suited to the smaller air-supported structure is the revolving door as this causes the least air loss. However, as it takes so much longer for a given number of people to pass through this type of door as compared to a conventional type, revolving doors are usually considered to be unsuitable from an escape point of view. When they are permitted, an additional door or opening must be provided, bringing more problems from air loss. Air-locks and air curtains are recognised means of access and exit, but they must conform to BS 6661 requirements. No exit width should be less than 800mm and, where the occupancy exceeds 100 persons this should be increased to 1100mm with extra width for every extra 100 persons. Travel distances are restricted and emergency lighting and exit signs conforming to BS 5266 Pt 1 are required

2 Underground and unfenestrated buildings

a. General

If involved in fire these types of premises are especially dangerous to both occupants and firefighters. Whether they are large sub-basements, systems of tunnels and caverns or above ground totally enclosed buildings, the problems are :

(i)   An absence of adequate means of venting the heat, smoke and toxic products of combustion;

(ii) a general lack of access and subsequent chance of disorientation;

(iii) difficulty in appraising the fire conditions or even finding the fire without risking firefighters in dangerous areas;

(iv) communications between firefighters and between them and the outside;

(v) application of extinguishing media;

(vi) congestion and restriction of movement within the space involved.

A CFBAC working party studied the subject and published its findings in FSC 4/1968. Their comments fell mainly into two groups – operational and fire prevention. Many of the points made have become standard practice in brigades eg. guide lines, communications and BA procedures.

b. Operational

Any fire in this type of premises brings extremely punishing conditions of excessive heat and humidity. This may require large numbers of BA wearers in order to keep the exposure of individual firefighters down to a tolerable level. Very strict control of BA procedure must be maintained. It is to be expected that any brigade having this type of premises in their area would pre-plan and hold regular exercises and/or visits so that firefighters likely to become involved have some knowledge of the risk. This knowledge could include :

(i)   difficult areas of communication;

(ii) alternative means of access;

(iii) water supplies;

(iv) position of internal doors, shutters and lifts;

(v) probable location of BA controls.

Some of the premises could be high security eg. MOD. Any difficulties in obtaining access or knowledge would be subject to negotiation. These must, obviously be carried out with the emphasis on the fact that the lives of LAFB firefighters are at risk.

c. Fire prevention

Generally, purpose-built premises of this sort would be compartmented, automatically protected and vented and organised to control hazardous storage. However, most of these premises are adaptations and the 1968 report recognised this and made recommendations accordingly. Amongst these were the following:

(i) effective control of the type of contents and isolation of the particularly hazardous elements;

(ii) if staff are present, adequate training in the use of the firefighting equipment eg. hose-reels, and extinguishers and how to raise the alarm;

(iii) the installation of automatic detection and adequate means of calling the brigade;

(iv) compartmentation, fire stopping etc. to be maintained to a high standard;

(v) adequate means of escape for the occupants;

(vi) plans of access etc. well indicated and available for firefighters;

(vii) where necessary, the installation of fixed automatic firefighting systems eg. sprinklers, foam, halons, powder.

(vi) plans of access etc. well indicated and available for the firefighters;

Part 6
Services in buildings

Most modern buildings are designed to include what are known as "services" eg. air-conditioning, heating lifts, dust extraction plants, electrical circuits. These will require roof or floor air-conditioning plants, boiler rooms, lift motor rooms, fans, electrical transformer rooms and, perhaps, "access floors" (see Chapter 13 Section 2). Often very large buildings or complexes are, as has already been stated, "intelligent". All services are centred on a control room which is usually manned although much of the equipment in the building will be self-monitoring. Some of these systems have already been dealt with elsewhere eg. fire venting systems in the Manual book 9, lifts in Book 12 and electricity and gas in Part 6b. This Part will concern itself with natural and mechanical ventilation, dust and solvent extraction, conveyors and machinery drives.

Chapter 16
Services in buildings

1 Natural and mechanical ventilation

a. Natural ventilation

In natural ventilation the circulation and renewal of the air inside a building is effected by a combination of wind entering from outside the building and air currents generated inside. Wind enters on the windward side through doors, windows and ventilators and is drawn out by suction on the leeward side and up chimneys even though there is no fire. Natural ventilation is greatly increased by the internal air currents set up by fires, radiators etc. and the natural warmth of the occupants. The warmed air rises and escapes through the tops of windows and high level ventilators, and cold air is drawn in to replace it through the doors and windows.

Many different types of air inlets and outlets have been used at different periods and in different kinds of buildings. They are all, in essence, simply holes in the outer wall or roof fitted with flaps, grilles or louvres to allow air to enter or escape and, at the same time, excluding rain and draughts. The type most commonly used today is known as an "air-brick" and is placed at high level as an outlet in rooms which have no chimney flue. It consists of a 230mm square opening in the wall protected on the inside and outside by grilles. Similarly air bricks are provided to ventilate the underside of a wooden ground floor where fitted, the air entering on the windward side, circulating round the house and out on the other side.

Low level air inlets are uncommon today but many old building have them, often screened by a metal tube which deflects the air upwards (see Fig 16.1). In many modern buildings, particularly offices and hotels, fresh air inlets are often provided behind radiators placed under windows.

Older single storey factories and large halls are often ventilated by means of lantern lights in a flat roof or louvred ventilators placed at the apex of a pitched roof. More modern factories may have automatic ventilators or louvres fitted some of which are rain sensitive. These can all provide useful control of smoke in a building but could tend to draw fire into a roof space.

b. Mechanical ventilation

In mechanical ventilation the circulation of air is assisted, or even carried out entirely, by a system of fans and ducting. It is used in many buildings such as warehouses, cinemas, theatres, offices etc. where

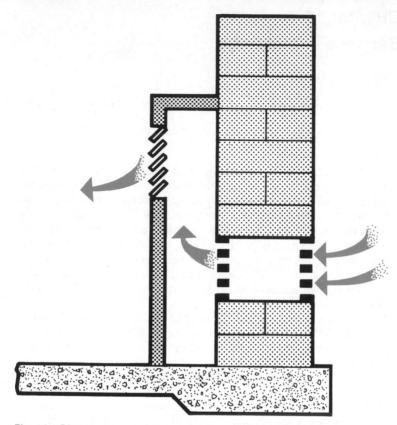

Fig. 16.1 Diagram showing the arrangement of a low level inlet.

large numbers of people congregate in a relatively small space. It is also used in factories where the occupants must be protected from harmful gases or dust produced in the manufacturing processes.

Mechanical ventilation can be divided into three principal groups:

(i)   where the vitiated air is extracted from the building by fans, fresh air finding its way in through doors and windows;

(ii) where fresh air is forced into the building by fans, vitiated air finding its way out through doors and windows;

(iii) where fans are used both to force fresh air into the building and to drive out vitiated air.

In the last two methods the air pressure inside the building is kept slightly above that outside so as to avoid incoming draughts ie.they are balanced systems. All mechanical systems include ducting, usually made from steel sheeting, which distributes or extracts the air.

Firefighters must be aware of the possibility of spread of fire or smoke throughout the building via these systems (see Manual Book 9, Chapter 21). Fig.16.2 shows, diagrammatically, an arrangement of the conditioning plant and parts of the ducting of a balanced system in a large premises.

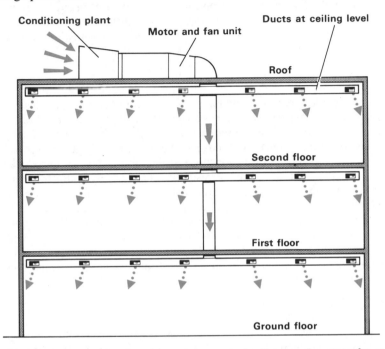

Fig. 16.2 Diagram showing the arrangement of a "plenum" system for an industrial premises.

2 Air conditioning systems

These systems are, in effect, extensions of ventilating systems in that they provide ventilation air which has been warmed or cooled and has the desired level of humidity.Basically an air conditioning system consists of;

(i)   fans for moving the air;

(ii)   filters for air cleansing;

(iii) refrigerating plant connected to heat exchange surfaces such as finned coils or chilled water sprays;

(iv)   means for warming the air;

(v)   means of humidfying the air;

(vi)   a control system to regulate the amount of heating or cooling automatically.

Depending on the type of use of the building some modern buildings have zoned systems (each zone having its own minisystem) but more usually the top floor is given over to the air-conditioning plant and the cleaned, heated/cooled, humidified air is circulated round the building from there.On their own these systems present little hazard and most systems will have automatic controls which operate whenever a fire situation is monitored or can be manually controlled from the central control room. Smoke is then either prevented from spreading around the building or, if required by the brigade, extracted.

3 Dust extraction

This is usually required by legislation in commercial or industrial premises to either protect the occupants from excessive inhalation of dust or the remove, or dilute a possible explosive hazard. Finely divided dust, of almost any kind, has the potential of extremely rapid flame propagation or explosion once an ignition source is introduced (see Manual Part 6c). Dust is usually collected, by extractor fans, through ducting to a collecting area. Any spark at the machine end can quickly be drawn along a duct and, as soon as it reaches the right mixture of oxygen and dust can cause an explosion. Quite often a minor explosion happens first which disturbs more dust and this larger cloud can cause a massive detonation. Any fire in a duct is dangerous and firefighters should attempt to cut off the forced draught first and then operate fixed sprinklers or introduce sprays in to the duct.

4 Fume extraction plants

In practically all processes involving chemicals, especially liquids eg. paint spraying, there will be a need to extract fumes in order to keep processes safe. In some cases the fumes may be recovered, processed themselves and stored or recirculated into the system. Here again automatic fire protection is usually required and safety regulations are strict. Fires do occur in the ducting and these are sometimes fitted with light panels either to vent an explosion or to enable access to be made to the duct. Firefighters should take care and follow a similar procedure as in 4 above not forgetting to cover any storage area.

5 Mechanical conveyors and chutes

a. Conveyor belts

Nowadays, most conveyor belts, and similar automatic methods of transporting goods, are highly sophisticated and are found not only in factories and warehouses but in shopping complexes and hypermarkets. Because they are constructed mainly with noncombustible materials they do not, generally, present a fire hazard. Regulations also expect a high degree of automatic protection where they penetrate fire-resisting walls and floors. Modern conveyors run on specially designed rollers which do not require grease or oil which eliminates one of the most prevalent causes of fires on belts. There is still the possibility of static electricity building up and, unless the earthing is sound, providing a source of ignition with sparks. Some older heavy-duty conveyors are still run on metal rollers and guides and the old hazard of grease build-up is still there. Firefighters should try to stop a conveyor if called to a fire on or near one because this prevents burning material being carried around a building. Occasionally fixed automatic sprinklers are fitted over the conveyor and these should be left operating until other firefighting media can be brought into use. An example of mass-transfer of goods is the high-bay warehouse described in Chapter 13 and others are in such industrial areas as vehicle manufacturers.Though not all strictly "belts" they are all practically continuous mass movement systems with similar problems of maintenance and possible overheating of motors etc.

b. Gravity feeds

Gravity feeds will be found either in the form of pipes or channel slides. Both forms are used in factories and warehouses. Piping is, of course, used for conveying industrial liquids from one part of a factory to another usually from tanks on upper floors or the roof. Such liquids as acids, alkalis and flammables used in industrial processes may be moved in this way. Obviously any leakage can lead to a very dangerous situation and firefighters should, wearing appropriate protective clothing, attempt to isolate the fracture by operating valves.

c. Suction pipes

Another method of mass transfer is by suction piping. Such materials as cement, grain, sugar, pulverised fuel, plastic pellets etc. are sucked out of the bulk transport eg. a ship's hold and fed, via piping, to their storage areas. Grain elevators and fuel silos are often filled in this way. As with any smallgrained material (see section 4) the danger is of a dust explosion and there are various systems preventing either the dust from attaining the right explosive mixture or of venting the pressure if it does explode.

Firefighters must take great care when working in, near or over any of these types of storage area. The use of BA would prevent dust from damaging the lungs but, more importantly, would provide air if a firefighter fell and was buried by a fall of the material. The use of lines attached to firefighters would also make it easier to trace anybody who fell into the material and to haul them out.

6 Machinery drives

Most machinery in commercial and industrial use is driven by electrical power. The feeding of the power varies from light 3-core cable, running a cloth cutter or tailor's iron to a heavy multi-core MICS cable powering a heavy crane.The design of the system is always peculiar to the task required to be done even to the point of requiring intrinsic safety eg. for explosive atmospheres.

Any fires involving this type of power-drive will usually be due to the overheating of the electrical motor. Most systems will have either an automatic cut-off for the power ie. an overload switch or a type of manual "punch" button to isolate the machine rapidly.

In large workshops containing a lot of machinery firefighters must move about with caution as machinery may still be running.

7 Heating systems

Heating systems in buildings, other than private houses, are by warm air or hot water systems. These are usually run from a boiler fired by gas, oil, solid fuel or, very occasionally, electricity. The systems are such that, in addition to usually being enclosed in a fire-resisting compartment, automatic safety devices are fitted which, in the event of dangerous conditions arising, will cut off the fuel supply and convey an alarm. The Manual Part 6c Section 5 illustrates some of these automatic devices.

Structure and publishing history of
Manual of Firemanship

The Manual of Firemanship was first published in a series of nine 'Parts' (1-5, 6a, 6b. 6c and 7) between 1943 and 1962.

In July 1974, it was decided that these nine Parts should be gradually replaced by 18 'Books' and a revised format for the *Manual* was drawn up. The new Books were to up-date the information given and arrange the subjects covered in more compact and coherent groups, each group occupying one of the new Books. The following pages show the original plan, *as amended to date*. Twelve of these Books have so far been published; the present volume is the second edition of Book 8.

Since 1974 there have been many developments in Fire Brigade practice and equipment and in the problems which firefighters may have to face. To remain an authoritative and up-to-date survey of the science of firefighting the Manual must take these developments into account. Not all the necessary changes can be accommodated within the format announced in 1974. The reader should therefore be aware that the structure of unpublished Books of the Manual, as set out on the following pages, is subject to change. Such changes will be publicised as far in advance as possible.

The next Book planned for publication is the second edition of Book 2 "Fire Service Equipment".

Manual of Firemanship

**Book 1 Elements of combustion and
extinction (published in 1974)**
Part
1 Physics of combustion
2 Chemistry of combustion
3 Methods of extinguishing fire

**Book 2 Fire Brigade equipment (published
in 1974)**
Part
1 Hose
2 Hose fittings
3 Ropes and lines, knots, slings, etc.
4 Small gear

**Book 3 (second edition) Hand pumps,
extinguishers and foam equipment
(published in 1988)**
Part
1 Hand-operated pumps
2 Portable fire extinguishers and fire blankets
3 Foam and foam-making equipment

**Book 4 Incidents involving aircraft,
shipping and railways (published in
1985)**
Part
1 Incidents involving aircraft
2 Incidents involving shipping
3 Incidents involving railways

**Book 5 Ladders and appliances published
in 1984)**
Part
1 Extension ladders, hook ladders and roof
ladders
2 Escapes
3 Turntable ladders
4 Hydraulic platforms
5 Special appliances
6 Pumping appliances

Book 6 (second edition) **Breathing apparatus and resuscitation (published in 1989)**
Part
1 Breathing apparatus
2 Operational procedure
3 Protective clothing
4 Resuscitation

Book 7 (second edition) **Hydraulics, pumps and pump operation (published in 1986)**
Part
1 Hydraulics
2 Water supplies and hydrants
3 Pumps and pump operation
4 Water carrying and relaying
Appendices

Book 8 Building constructions and structural fire protection (published in 1992)
Part
1 Building materials
2 Elements of structure
3 Building design
4 Interior fire loading
5 Examples of buildings
6 Services in buildings

Book 9 Fire protection of buildings (published in 1990)
Part
1 Fire extinguishing systems
2 Fire alarm systems
3 Fire venting systems

Book 10 Fire Brigade communications and mobilising (published in 1991)
Part
1 The public telephone system and its relationship to the Fire Service
2 Mobilising arrangements
3 Methods of controlling call-out systems
4 Radio
5 Automatic fire alarm signalling system arrangements
6 Future developments

Book 11 Practical firemanship I (published in 1981)
Part
1 Practical firefighting
2 Methods of entry into buildings
3 Control at a fire

Book 12   Practical firemanship 11 (published in 1983)

Part
1 Fire Service rescues
2 Decontamination
3 Ventilation of fires
4 Salvage
5 After the incident

Book 13
Contents not yet decided

Book 14   Special fires I (not yet published) *Information available in*

Part	Part	Chapter	Last impression
1 Fires in aminal and vegetable oils	*6c*	*45(8)*	*1986*
2 Fires in fats and waxes	*6c*	*45(3)*	*1986*
3 Fires in resins and gums	*6c*	*45(13)*	*1986*
4 Fires in grain, hops, etc	*6c*	*45(6)*	*1986*
5 Fires in fibrous materials	*6c*	*45(4)*	*1986*
6 Fires in sugar	*6c*	*45(15)*	*1986*
7 Fires in paint and varnishes	*6c*	*45 (9)*	*1986*

Book 14   Special fires II (not yet published) *Information available in*

Part	Part	Chapter	Last impression
1 Fires in dust	*6c*	*45(1)*	*1986*
2 Fires in explosive	*6c*	*45(2)*	*1986*
3 Fires in metals	*6c*	*45(7)*	*1986*
4 Fires in plastics	*6c*	*45(10)*	*1986*
5 Fires involving radioactive materials	*6c*	*45(11)*	*1986*
6 Fires in refrigeration plant	*6c*	*45(12)*	*1986*
7 Fires in rubber	*6c*	*45(14)*	*1986*

Book 16   Special fires I (not yet published) *Information available in*

Part	Part	Chapter	Last impression
1 Fires in rural areas	*6c*	*1*	*1975*
2 Fires in electricity undertakings	*6c*	*3*	*1975*

Book 17   Special fires IV (not yet published) *Information available in*

Part	Part	Chapter	Last impression
1 Fires in fuels	*6c*	*45(5)*	*1986*
2 Fires in oil refineries	*6c*	*5*	*1975*
3 Fires in gas works	*6c*	*2*	*1975*

Book 18   Contents not yet decided

Printed in the United Kingdom for HMSO
Dd 301886 12/95 C85 59226